Catering for

HEALTH AND SPECIAL DIETS

A HANDBOOK FOR EVERY HOME COOK

Maurice Newbound

G. S. PUBLICATIONS
CHARDSTOCK HOUSE CHARD
SOMERSET TA20 2TL ENGLAND

FRONT COVER PICTURE: The cover picture depicts the central theme of this book. Almost any diet can be satisfied by a meal with only the "savoury" being changed.

Our picture shows 'Toad in the Hole', a new product by Haldane Foods under its Vegetable Feasts brand and available frozen as a vegetarian savoury.

Acknowledgements

Although the author of any book may at times feel like a pioneer, keen to press all the points and anxious that the message should be heard, it is often the help of others that finally creates the end product. In this I have had plenty of help . Naturally our mutual interest throughout has been the fascinating subject of catering for health and special diets.

While I do most sincerely thank all those who helped, may I in particular thank Joan Power for sticking at the Word Processor and the constant updating of files and research. My thanks also to Charmian Barnes for her work as Librarian and co-ordinator of the Buyer's Guide.

To Terry Wright at our local printers, Mark Curnock at the typesetters who have remained, as always, calm in the process of producing the finished product. To Roy Hewetson, Jane Waters, Lesley Wilson, Sue Smith, Steve Parsons, Dr. Rosy (Thomson) Daniel, Katherine Monbiot, Nikki Holley, Toni Simons, Paul Crowder, Sandra Gibbons, Gwynne Davies, Paul Webster, Sue Kreitzman, Ramesh B. Patel, Keith Squires of Life Foundation, Colin Southam of Ace Communications, Robert Burton for his kind help on the complications of transferring copy to the appropriate printers disk, and all my many friends who have encouraged me and stuck with the concept to completion.

I acknowledge Gloria Hoare for her earlier administration work and Rosy Rabson who worked with me on the original concept when at times it seemed that we often went two paces forward and three back, and all the many organisations that have vetted, amended and corrected my many drafts including the Vegetarian Society, the Coeliac Society, The British Diabetic Association, the Vegan Society, the Jewish Vegetarian Society and The Natural Health Network.. Above all I have to thank my wife Shirley for her very practical help and support throughout.

BCFTCS

£5·95

Catering for

HEALTH
AND
SPECIAL
DIETS

First published in Great Britain in 1992 by
G S Publications
Chardstock House
Chard
Somerset TA20 2TL
England
Tel: 0460 63229 Fax: 0460 63809

Cover Design by Mark Stevens
Set in Helvetica by Character Graphics, Taunton, Somerset
Printed by The Matthews Wright Press, Chard, Somerset

British Library Cataloguing in Publication Data
A catalogue record for this is available
from the British Library

ISBN 0-9520502-0-X

**This book is dedicated to everyone who enjoys a special diet meal
and those that prepare it.**

NOTE: All editorial, recipes, and Buyer's Guide information is
given in good faith and provided only to give an overview of
the type of diets that the reader may encounter. Neither the
publishers nor the author accept any responsibility for any
effects that may arise from giving or taking any diet or advice
given in this book. Any reader contemplating taking or giving
any diet should first seek qualified professional advice.

Contents

CATERING FOR HEALTH & SPECIAL DIETS

The concept of this book has been welcomed by many. Here are just some of the comments received:

"What a relief! We finally have a map to guide our patients – and their families – through the tricky terrain of special diets"
Dr Rosy (Thomson) Daniel
Holistic Director at Bristol Cancer Help Centre

'This book will be a boon for every home cook. It gets to the heart of catering for special diets and will be welcomed by the millions of vegetarians in the U.K."
The Vegetarian Society

"Increasing awareness that food plays an important role in our health and well-being can create a dilemma for those needing to adjust their diet or prepare and cook for a family where the needs of one member is different. It certainly can cause anxiety if you need to cater for a guest with special dietary needs. 'Catering for Health & Special Diets' guides you through the maze of information currently available in a clear and concise way. Whatever your dietary needs, I thoroughly recommend this book".
Jane Waters, Director of The Alternative Centre, London

"In my opinion this book is one of the most important in its field to have been published in recent years. Written in an easy to read style it covers every aspect of catering for those with special dietary needs."
Colin Southam, Public Relations Consultant in the health food industry.

"A very useful resource for anyone requiring special dietary information."
Batchelors Nutritional Advice Centre

"At last we have a book that caters for special dietary needs that everyone will be able to understand without having a degree in food nutrition. Well done and thank you."
Nigel G. Phillips, Managing Director, granoVita UK Ltd.
(Health food manufacturer)

"Books to assist those with dietary problems are always welcome and the scope of 'Catering for Health & Special Diets' should make it a must for both professionals and lay people involved in the subject."
Michelle Berridale-Johnson, Berrydales
(Specialist food manufacturers)

Introduction

For many years I have been unable to eat meat due to a very bad allergic reaction. Travelling around the UK and Europe, I discovered just how difficult it was for the many people who had to avoid certain foods when staying with friends or at hotels. It was a worry for the person preparing the meal and this anxiety was passed on to the person at the receiving end.

Slowly I came to realise two factors. The first was that I was not alone in requiring a 'special' diet, in fact there are many millions of us. The second factor was that the problem of catering for almost any diet could be solved very easily. This is accomplished simply by understanding the different diets and, once that understanding is in place, it is often not necessary to change the whole meal - only the meat or fish portion plus, of course, any dressings that offend the particular diet.

In addition, I soon found out that because of growing demand there was an increasing number of ready mixed special diet meals available. This makes life very easy for those home cooks who want a quick answer to that unexpected special diet guest.

Despite this, I so often found people very anxious when a member of their family required a diet which cut out one of the 'normal' key products. I recall one parent telling me that her son had become a vegetarian, "and I just do not know what to give him". It only took a little time to give reassurance. Generally, it was simply a case of mentioning that the replacement of the meat, or fish, was by a 'savoury', either from one of the wonderful vegetarian cook books available or by buying this from a health food shop or supermarket. I knew that it would be sensible and helpful to provide a book on the subject.

However, one of the reasons encouraging me finally to press ahead with this book was the comments of a professional caterer (a restaurant owner) who appeared to have some out-dated ideas. What made it all the more interesting was that he claimed to be well trained and was quite young and therefore not, I would have thought, set in his ways.

Let's look at his first comment, spoken in a high-handed manner. It was that he would be willing to provide meals for vegetarians "providing they gave advance notice". I could hardly believe my ears and later drew him to one side and suggested, as gently as possible, that he was talking nonsense. Surely, I suggested, he was aware of the hundreds of products now available, both in bulk and small packs, which can be kept in stock for these customers' meals. I explained that, quite apart from the availability of these products, customers or guests did not have to be vegetarian to enjoy vegetarian food. Today most caterers have at least one good vegetarian meal on their menu as part of their range for anyone who would like to have an alternative to meat or fish.

With vegan or gluten-free meals he might have been excused if he felt there was a difficulty but, even here, he would be wrong.......THERE IS NO MAJOR DIFFICULTY .....are YOU surprised? If so, you will find the following pages of great interest.

As this edition is primarily aimed at the home cook, you may feel that the example I have given may not be entirely applicable for you. You will, however, find that the same points made and others touching on professional catering in the various chapters within this book still apply to you at home.

While many will insist on creating their own 'savouries' for the main meal (see the recipe section) others will simply buy one of the many products that can be kept in store for that unexpected guest.

Let's get down to some facts

It is estimated that over 10 million people in the UK are on special diets. People are becoming vegetarian at the rate of 28,000 PER

WEEK! THE DAYS OF BEING THOUGHT A 'CRANK' ARE OVER. If you still want to think that way you could be the loser. To provide good, healthy diet food is today's pattern and, once you accept that, it can be fun! Let me tell you a true story.

I live near two pubs that serve lunch-time and evening meals. One proprietor declares that there is no demand for special dietary meals and usually has a half-empty restaurant section. He does not provide meals for vegetarians or, when he does, there is no confidence given that they are without some meat or fish ingredient. He appears not to care and special diets are a nuisance. Even if there is a group of customers with one vegetarian he will simply trot out the old offer of a salad. He reflects an old-time approach to catering.

The other pub is full every lunch-time and evening, and many of these customers want special dietary meals. This pub provides a full menu of vegan and vegetarian meals and is scrupulous about not mixing ingredients or utensils.

The story is really as short as I have set out but the background is complex. The first pub has never really taken the trouble to understand special diets or how those requiring them think on the subject. The other pub has. At home we can learn the lessons very quickly on how to greet and serve guests or members of the family who do have a dietary need.

This book sets out to tell you how attitudes, and a little understanding, can produce good, healthy, acceptable food for any guest, which is prepared and served in a relaxed way.

When you have read this guide, if you do not already provide alternatives to your range of meat and two veg I am quite sure you will want to. If you get one idea or helpful hint from these pages, it will be worth the very modest investment. However, I believe you will discover a whole new, fascinating world which will bring many moments of enjoyment as you gain understanding and when you cater for others with special requirements.

How to use this book

I have tried to make 'Catering for Health & Special Diets' interesting as well as useful in catering for others. At home you should enjoy the challenge of providing meals for those who have a particular eating or drinking requirement and this is one of the aims of the book.

It should be used as a source of reassurance. Reassurance both for those providing the meal and those having the pleasure of enjoying it. Of course it can also serve as a type of 'training manual' for some, or simply as a point of reference for others.

As I expect the book to be picked up for quick reference you will find within the different sections a number of duplications. It is not intended as a book to be read from cover to cover at one sitting, although this may happen.

It is a well known learning concept that every key point should be repeated three times to get maximum understanding. I have not set out to do that but where I have repeated points this has been done for a reason; the main one being simply to press home a particular point for greater understanding. This is so important to ensure the greatest empathy with your guest. Of course, it need not be a 'guest' in the normal sense. It could be that one of your children, or your spouse, decides to eat a particular diet.

To get the best out of this book I would recommend you first study the Contents page and then quickly glance through the publication. There are a number of organisations that provide home cook training sessions within the U.K. and if you are using the book after training then you will be influenced by that learning. Otherwise I recommend you should simply refer to sections of the book when the need arises.

A Buyer's Guide can never be fully complete. Every day new products are being developed and others are withdrawn. New firms start up as the growth of the market expands. However, the Buyer's Guide does have a good selection of firms willing to help you with products suitable for healthy eating or special diets. No doubt my records will grow and you are invited to tell me about firms and products you feel are suitable and should be included in the next edition.

LET US KNOW

In reverse, I would invite you to let me know of those products, or firms, that are listed but which you feel should not be included in the buying list. You will also find most retailers, especially health food stores, helpful and, if you are stuck for a savoury for that special vegan or gluten-free guest, you are certain to find on their shelves a suitable product. If you can't find what you need in the Buyer's Guide, or from your friendly retailer, use the reader enquiry form at the back.

I hope you will enjoy using 'Catering for Health & Special Diets' and would be pleased to have any constructive comments on how to improve the contents of future editions.

One final comment on getting the best out of this book. If you are not in empathy with those who eat differently to you it may be difficult to get the full benefit of the following chapters and the numerous hints and ideas. It is therefore worth deciding not to judge the merit of any special diet but just to accept that they (your guests) have a very good reason for following their diet which may be difficult to fully appreciate. After studying this book that should no longer be a problem.

Chapter 1

THE AIM OF THIS BOOK

The aim of this book is a simple one: to help you to provide acceptable healthy food for people who may require meals linked to particular diets. At the same time you are encouraged to benefit from providing your guests with their special dietary requirements. This manual will help you to serve them without causing them embarrassment.

Through the Buyer's Guide section, which lists many of the suppliers of products and services for diets and healthy eating generally, you will benefit from the information provided. Variety is important in diets and the Buyer's Guide will highlight the manufacturers of the wide range of products available.

It should be clear what this book is NOT aiming to do.

Firstly, it is NOT seeking to convert you, or your visitors, to any special diet, nor to convince you to become either vegetarian or vegan (a full description is published in Chapters 3 and 4). Of course this may happen as there is plenty of food for thought in this book, but that is not the primary intention. The main purpose is to ensure you have the possibility of understanding the background to these particular diets and, thereby, provide meals that satisfy those requirements.

Secondly, it does NOT seek to convince you of the value of a "healthy" diet, nor to bombard you with cliches such as "You are what you eat". What you eat is your own business. If as a result of using this book you become interested in eating more healthily that's fine, but our aim is that you are encouraged to provide healthy meals for others.

Thirdly, it does NOT set out to offer you an exhaustive collection of recipes. In the recipe section you will find a selection of some "special diet" recipes, which concentrate on simplicity, nutritional content and excellence of presentation and flavour. Every recipe is tried, tested and tasty. But this book is much more than just a cookbook for the home cook. Many of the recipes are there to illustrate the possibilities for providing attractive and satisfying meals to those who appear to have a difficult and restrictive diet. What, for instance, do you provide for a person on a vegan diet who does not want salad? This diet prohibits all meat and fish products and all dairy products, such as cheese, milk and eggs. The book will clearly illustrate that there are plenty of ready mixed products if you do not want to start preparing your own meals. Should you feel determined to start from scratch, and put together all the ingredients, there are plenty of options in the recipe section. The most important point I want to make is that to provide for those who require a meal based on a special diet should pose no problems once you have read this book.

Fourthly, it is not intended to be a comprehensive medical handbook. Those trained in such matters will have spent many years in study and are well aware of the whole range of dietetic practices. Publications for further reading are listed and, if you have a medical problem, it would make sense to see a qualified specialist. Organisations covering this subject are listed at the back.

WHY HEALTHY AND SPECIAL DIETS?

There is nothing cranky, faddy or difficult about people with special dietary needs. Nor is there anything strange about people wanting healthy food. Basically they fall into two groups:

Medical Needs

For some people, there is a medical need to avoid certain foods completely. Diabetics have to watch their diets. The same goes for sufferers from coeliac disease, who are allergic to even the tiniest quantity of gluten in their food and must avoid bread, cakes, etc, for the rest of their lives. There are less well known allergies too. Some people, after years of suffering, have found that by avoiding certain foods - often dairy products which aggravate their condition - they are able to lead a normal life again.

But so sensitive is their system to the offending food that just one small particle can bring back the symptoms immediately.

Such people are not cranky in their rejection of certain foods: a few crumbs can cause untold suffering.

Religious, Moral and Environmental Issues
Many people have powerful moral or religious objections to certain foods. Muslim children in this country learn at a very early age to read the ingredients panel on crisp packets, to make sure their crisps contain no pork products. Jews, who must not mix meat and milk, use kosher margarine rather than butter in their beef sandwiches. These two groups of people are not being "difficult", any more than a convinced teetotaller or a reformed alcoholic is being difficult in requiring alcohol-free drinks. Yet far too often a request for a meal which is free from dairy products (for vegans or arthritics) or gluten (for coeliac sufferers) is met by blank stares, and vegetarians are offered "vegetable" soup made from meat stock. This is as inexcusable as attempting to force a gin and tonic on a reformed alcoholic.

YOU CAN COPE!
If you look up "cope" in the dictionary you will find a definition along the lines of "deal successfully with a situation or problem". That is what you, with the help of this book, are going to do.

Coping with special dietary requirements is not intrinsically difficult. It is a matter of understanding the principles behind each diet. 'Catering for Health and Special Diets' (C.H.S.D.) sets out to explain the various special dietary needs you are likely to come across, and suggests ways of meeting them, with enjoyable results for all concerned.

A MATTER OF UNDERSTANDING
These days more and more people are unwilling or unable to eat everything put before them. Despite this growing trend, the arrival of a guest with special dietary requirements can throw even the most experienced provider into confusion and anxiety.

Away with confusion. Once explained, special dietary needs cease to be "special" and become simple and obvious. Coping with them becomes an everyday matter rather than a cause for anxiety. There has always been a special relationship between the person who provides a meal and the person who consumes it. With mutual understanding and trust, provider and consumer can relax and enjoy the experience together. Like taking the trouble to learn a few words of a foreign language before going abroad on holiday, a little understanding of special dietary needs will make you many friends.

While 'C.H.S.D.' is written with the 'home cook' particularly in mind, its contents are equally applicable for public catering in hotels, pubs, canteens, hospitals, airports, aircraft, ships, restaurants, schools, etc.

With the growing understanding of the role of diet in the management of various disorders, coupled with the rapid rise in vegetarianism and veganism, the likelihood that you will at some time have to cater for a "special" guest is very strong indeed.

People responsible for providing "special" meals do not need to follow that diet themselves, but they MUST show guests that they understand their requirements. If they profess to offer food suited to a particular dietary need, then what they offer must be "safe" at all stages of preparation. So, for example, a stew for a coeliac sufferer will be thickened with cornflour, potato, arrowroot or brown rice flour rather than wheat flour.

"What the eye does not see, the heart does not grieve about" most emphatically does not apply in the world of coping with special diets. How can vegetarian guests relax and enjoy their meal if they are worrying about the possibility of meat stock that may lurk in vegetable soup, or if the person on a vegan diet is worrying about egg or other dairy products in their nut roast? You MUST show them that you know their needs and can be trusted to meet them.

AND HERE IS THE GOOD NEWS

Now let's get this into proportion. It is not usually necessary to offer a completely different meal to a "special" guest. For those who are suddenly confronted with a guest or member of the family who requires a meal linked with one of the diets mentioned in this book, it can be a moment of anxiety. Many get into a panic because they think the whole meal has to be changed. I have seen this happen hundreds of times. There are several reasons for this mental block which, over the years has programmed in our minds that vegetarians must live on salads and goodness knows what is left for a vegan to eat!!

In many diets listed, only a small part of the meal will need to be replaced, often the meat or fish in the main course. For the purpose of clarity, I shall refer throughout this book to that replacement of the meat or fish part of the menu as a "savoury". This "savoury" will vary according to the experience and knowledge of the provider and the special needs of the guests. Providers will find plenty of ideas for delicious "savouries" in this book, which will help to expand their repertoire from, for example, the usual "nice omelette or cheese salad" which vegetarians are invariably offered in lieu of meat or fish. It is, of course, necessary to watch sauces and gravies. Not much point in providing an acceptable savoury if the dressing is out of keeping with the diet.

An example of a savoury in every day use is Ratatouille, but it could be a vegetable burger, a lentil pie or any of the savouries in the recipe section. There are numerous exciting products supplied through the manufacturers listed in our Buyer's Guide.

As mentioned in my guidance notes on how to use this manual, do be prepared for duplication throughout as I have to allow for readers just checking a single chapter for an urgent need.

Chapter Two

THE BENEFITS OF UNDERSTANDING

*E*veryone benefits when an appetizing and acceptable meal is served to someone on a special diet. The guest enjoys the experience and is grateful. The provider enjoys the guest's thanks and appreciation and the satisfaction of a job well done. In any private household this is gratifying for its own sake but it has many benefits that may be hidden.

Hospitals and nursing homes are, of course, keenly aware of the need to provide a diet to suit the individual. They understand what an important part food plays in the recovery of their patients. There is a growing understanding of the necessity for satisfying special dietary needs in an unobtrusive but caring way, so that patients, feeling comfortable with their diets, can relax, enjoy their meals and concentrate on getting well again. You may well feel that your house is not a hospital but very often it becomes a 'nursing' home. Today there is a great possibility that one of your family will feel it helpful for health, or some particular illness, to require a special diet. It will be then that you will be pleased that you have this book to turn to. The benefits in having that empathy with your guest or member of the family will be very clear.

CATERING FOR PRIVATE PARTIES OR WHEN GUESTS CALL

In private homes it is important that guests or members of the family do not feel they are a nuisance. The host usually receives advance warning about "special" guests and may be able to adjust the whole meal to suit everyone. One successful hostess has a firm rule: if someone on a special diet eats at her table,

Mrs R provides scrupulously for that guest's needs, then serves the same meal without comment or explanation to EVERYONE.

"If Bill needs to avoid wheat flour" (or meat, or sugar, or whatever) "all the time, then we can all jolly well do the same while he's here," she says firmly.

The meal is always delicious and nobody who was not in the know would guess that there was anything "special" about it. This is, therefore, how one reader deals with guests on special diets. By the time you finish this book many other ideas will be apparent and the choice on how you use this information will be yours.

Many organisers of conferences work towards the same approach as Mrs. R. For example, one conference which has a fair number of vegetarians and vegans attending, actually provides vegan meals to everyone without comment and usually gets a round of applause for the quality of food for the three day event.

"I'M ON A SPECIAL DIET - CAN YOU COPE?"

These words should start a chain of communication and understanding in catering for special diets. Each of our chapters will lead you through this communication pattern. But do bear in mind it can be for some like learning to drive a car. At first the individual parts of the communication can appear clumsy and contrived yet, as you relax and project that relaxation to your guest, the questions which are part of the process become not only natural but are seen to be helpful.

BE A GOOD LISTENER

Most people on special diets are used to explaining their needs to the uninformed. A good host will listen attentively and then, if a particular thing is NOT available, admit as much and tactfully suggest an alternative within the guidelines of the diet.

So much for the first link in the chain of understanding and communication. Next, if the person learning of the special needs is not the person doing the actual preparation, the message must pass reliably along the chain to someone who can be trusted to meet those needs at all stages of providing the meal and service.

Breakdowns in communication are inexcusable and in the case of "medical" diets may even prove fatal.

Everyone involved in catering for special diets - every link in the chain - must have a broad understanding of what is involved. There is no need for a deep and detailed knowledge of every aspect of every diet, but rather a willingness to listen, to learn, to be flexible and to care. One household I know keeps an address book with names and dietary requirements. "Then one doesn't upset anyone. It's all a matter of good manners really " states the hostess.

SEPARATION OF INGREDIENTS

"One man's meat is another man's poison." - old proverb. We have all heard of strict kosher homes where separate sets of utensils are kept for the preparation of dairy products and meat. It could be essential for you if you are to cater for all types of diets in one area. One large caterer decided to have different coloured serving spoons. Red for vegan, white for vegetarian and green for meat.

Few kitchens at present aspire to such an ideal. All the same, one has to realise that when vegetarians say "no meat or fish" they mean just that: no meat or fish, or meat and fish products at any stage of preparation. That means frying in vegetable oil and using vegetable stocks (see chapters on vegetarian and vegan diets). Likewise, it is no use including a little green pepper in a dish for someone who is allergic to it, and saying "I'm sure your system will cope with that amount." It won't (see Chapter 5 which deals with allergies).

It is all, once again, a matter of good manners and understanding – the kind of understanding that goes beyond one's own dietary needs and preferences. This brings an appreciation that what may be acceptable for you may be – literally or metaphorically - another person's poison.

THE HIDDEN BENEFITS

One of the benefits of providing for a special diet is the pleasure of a satisfied guest with all that rubs off from that. This awareness of your ability to satisfy your guest or your family will give everyone a warm and pleasing feeling.

At home you will also find greater satisfaction and an appreciation by your guests of the options they have available. An essential part of this enjoyment is a full understanding of the importance of catering for those special diets.

Overall, the benefits of understanding just go on and on. The more you learn, the more enjoyable it becomes and the greater the appreciation of the variety of starters, savouries and desserts that are available to you today from a retailer if you do not have the time, the experience or the wish to create your own. Quite apart from the well known supermarkets that all carry a variety of dietary products, your local health shop specialises in these items and will always be pleased to help you.

Chapter Three

THE VEGETARIAN DIET

*T**he word 'vegetarian' was first coined in 1842. The name was derived from the Latin word 'vegetus'. It means "whole, sound, fresh, or lively", as in the Latin term 'homo vegetus' meaning a mentally and physically vigorous person.***

There is an ever increasing number of vegetarians (currently estimated at 3.6 million), plus a large number of people who often choose meat-free wholefood meals. A recent figure given for people becoming vegetarian is 28,000 every week! A vegetarian is someone who does not eat meat (that includes poultry) or fish (that includes seafood, i.e. prawns, crab etc.) nor indeed any slaughter house by-product like gelatine.

In many cases a vegetarian meal is simply a meal with the meat or fish part replaced by a vegetarian or vegan 'savoury'. However, this chapter goes into some detail which should help those called upon to provide 'vegetarian' meals for others. It is important to understand that even experts disagree on what should comprise a vegetarian diet.

Many claim that a 'real' vegetarian is actually unwilling to eat anything which comes from the animal world, and this includes all dairy products and eggs but, for the sake of clarity, this is referred to as a 'vegan diet' in this book and is fully covered in the next chapter. It is this possible confusion which means you will often have to ask if someone is vegan or vegetarian.

Just to compound the situation, some self-styled 'vegetarians' avoid meat but eat fish. In other instances, they avoid red meat only. These are NOT vegetarians. Clearly this diet calls for very basic questions right from the start. Done properly, it can be quite casual in approach, yet it is *essential* to get this information to ensure a fully satisfied guest. It is also important that friends bringing a vegetarian to dinner feel comfortable with how their colleague is treated.

An example of this would be five people coming for dinner where one is vegetarian. Every care must be taken to ensure they are all treated as equals and served at the same time. While this example, and some others in this chapter, may be somewhat over-simplified, it is better to start with the basics and ask the indulgence of those readers who already have some experience in preparing for vegetarian diets. The following notes will help you achieve your aim of giving a good impression to everyone around the table.

HOW TO ACQUIRE THE BASIC INFORMATION

Obtaining basic information often begins when you first learn of any special dietary requirements of your guests.

You might perhaps simply ask the person requesting a vegetarian meal if they require a 'vegan' or a 'vegetarian' menu. One person out of ten may be rather surprised at being asked this but most will appreciate the question, and it will put you in a good light as regards both your knowledge and attitude. If the answer is "vegan", then this is fully covered in the next chapter. If the answer is "vegetarian" then you may need a supplementary question which will eventually come quite naturally. Your question on vegan or vegetarian will almost certainly have provided a fairly full answer as the reply will normally bring forth information beyond your original enquiry. If not, you will then ask if the person is a 'strict' vegetarian or just does not eat meat. *The way the question is asked is important,* since, as we now know, a vegetarian is a person who does not eat flesh of any description and that includes meat, poultry AND fish!

If the answer is just meat don't be surprised if a so-called no meat eater chooses poultry, for often they just do not eat 'red' meat. I repeat these are NOT vegetarians even if they insist on calling themselves one. Apart from recognising that fact there is no need to refer to this false claim. The name given to those who avoid red meat and occasionally eat poultry, fish and other animal products is 'Demi' Vegetarian. The person who avoids ALL meat, fish and poultry but includes milk, milk products and eggs is often called 'Lacto- ovo - Vegetarian'. Finally the person who ALSO avoids eggs but still takes milk and milk products is referred to as 'Lacto- Vegetarian'. So you see how confusing it all is!

REASON FOR BEING VEGETARIAN
It may be appropriate to pause now and reflect on why some people adopt a vegetarian diet. The most common reason is because they do not believe in having any animals killed for food. Indeed this belief often goes beyond this into other related aspects of lifestyle. However, we should NOT presume this to be the case, for it could be medical or linked with their religion.

Most vegetarians have chosen their diet on compassionate or ecological grounds (i.e. one acre of land provides ten times more food as crops than from grazing). They are normally also health, (and beauty), conscious. If you are not vegetarian yourself you may not have thought much about the wider implications of a vegetarian diet. Once explained, these often seem obvious. Without that basic understanding it is possible to make errors.

An example I often quote is the egg mayonnaise served as a starter for a vegetarian. Over the top was sprinkled small pieces of ham. The guest complained about this.

"Sorry, please leave the ham on the side of the plate" said the Head Waiter, who obviously had no concept of the magnitude of his blunder nor how he had compounded it.

Let us examine this for a moment. In the first place, why was the ham there? If you ask the chef in catering establishments as I have done, the replies tend to show a lack of understanding of the vege-tarian diet. They are usually along the lines of: "It added colour or flavour to the dish". If you feel this is fair comment then read the fol-lowing carefully as it is not the QUANTITY that matters but the fact that the food has been 'CONTAMINATED' in the first place.

Vegetarians, as we have stated, are unable to take meat or fish products. Some cannot support the killing of animals for their food. To put any form of 'flesh' (meat, poultry or fish) on a vege-tarian plate is, at best, an embarrassment and at worst an insult. But it goes much further than this .

Once the body's system gets used to doing without meat or fish, vegetarians are anxious to keep their systems free of what they consider contains   toxins. They are often physically and mentally repulsed by their meal being contaminated in this way.

NOT USING THE SAME UTENSILS

You should not use the same utensils for meat and vegetarian food without washing them between use. In some cases, even this is not sufficient and some diets require that the same utensils are never used. This is why some vegetarians, when eating out at a catering establishment, prefer to eat only at vegetarian restaurants. Here they know that a spoon just used for serving steak and kidney pie will not then be plunged into the nut roast to serve the vegetarian guest. (The section on allergies will clarify this point.) However, the home cook should have no problem in selecting different utensils if there is a mixed meal of, say, meat for some guests and vegetarian for others.

SOME REASSURANCE IS NEEDED

A vegetarian should also feel comfortable in accepting a vegetable soup as a starter. Experience has taught those on a special diet that unless they are eating at a vegetarian home, there *may* be hidden dangers lurking in the kitchen. Some reassurance is needed! For example you may need to convey clearly that no meat stock is used in your vegetable soup and not to assume that they know that. Some people have been known to take a high-handed approach as host and if asked about, say, meat stock, express the fact that surely the guest need not ask once they have said they are vegetarian. Such high-handedness is not justified when you know the number of times this is overlooked and the guest only knows about this when they start to taste the soup. Embarrassment is surely the order of the day from that point.

When we deal with allergies later in this book, we shall see that even a small drop of a substance to which people are allergic may spark off trouble.

Likewise for a vegetarian it is not a matter of quantity (as with the sprinkled ham on eggs) but rather that the meal has no meat, fish or fowl *products* at all. For them the need to keep *all* fish and meat products out of a 'vegetable' soup, is paramount. So this cuts out products like lard, suet, some margarines etc. The only way is to use a vegetable stock which can either be made in the kitchen or can be purchased. Some of these products are covered in the Buyer's Guide section of this book and include vegetable Oxo cube, Friggs, and others.

HEALTH AND ALLERGIES
Another reason for people cutting out all meat products from their diet or becoming vegetarian involves health. This happened in my own case. I had a major health problem for over three years and it was only resolved by excluding all meat products. Many health diets call for the elimination of meat, especially red meat. One of the reasons for this is the increasing use of chemicals used both on the grazing areas and in animal feeding products. Over the past twenty years or so this has become so common that most meat and poultry bears little relationship to what it was fifty years or so ago. This has not been helped by the vast broiler chicken industry that has been developed. Whereas the immune system can cope with normal food, even poor food at times, it has great difficulty in coping with the toxins found in some meats and poultry. The result is that some of us have become allergic to meat and our digestive systems have become over-sensitive to it.

WHOLE FOOD INGREDIENTS
It is also worth noting that those who have chosen a vegetarian diet usually prefer wholefood ingredients i.e. wholemeal flour and bread instead of white; organic vegetables, organic brown rice and not white rice etc. (See chapters 9 and 10).

To summarise:
(A)   Ask if vegan or vegetarian.
(B)   Ask if strict vegetarian or just a non-meat eater, only if the reply to first question does not provide the answer.
(C)   If there is a mixed group to cater for do not alter the rest of meal or offer salad when this is not also offered to the non-vegetarians in the party. At times it would appear that some hosts cannot accept that *Vegetarians do eat the same supporting vegetables*

as non-vegetarians!! It sounds crazy but you may well have been present at some celebration dinners, which include a wonderful selection of steaming hot vegetables, for those not on a particular diet and, while all this is being displayed, the vegetarian is offered salad. It does not make sense but it still goes on today.

Of course, vegetarians eat salad the same as non-vegetarians but this does not mean they do not enjoy hot vegetables along with a savoury in place of the meat or fish part of the meal.

(D) Keep all utensils separate as between vegetarian meals and non-vegetarian meals.

(E) Try not to make a fuss about this issue. Catering for a vegetarian diet should not be projected as a hassle or produce any over play.

(F) Replace the meat or fish portion with a 'savoury'. (See our Buyer's Guide or the savouries on sale at the supermarket or health food shop.)

(G) Watch out for meat and fish products in starters and side dishes.

Savouries

Having established the ground rules, now let us look at some ideas for the savoury which can replace meat and fish in the main course. Some recipes are given in Chapter 7 but here is a list of possibilities for you to create just to get you in the mood:

1. Ratatouille (with tofu or beans if protein is required)
2. Stuffed peppers or aubergine.
3. Walnut and mushroom casserole
4. Stuffed garlic mushrooms.
5. Lasagne (with vegetarian cheese).

Some of the titles given to savouries you can buy are 'Lentil and Vegetable Casserole', 'Mexican Bean Stew', 'Nut Roast', 'Burger Mix', 'Lentil Roast', 'Mushroom Roast', Sunflower and Sesame Roast', 'Mock Duck', etc., etc.

Starters and Desserts

There is no need to do other than reassure you on these and touch upon some likely problem areas. Armed with the basic strategy, you know you cannot go wrong on the vegetarian diet.

The vegan diet is a little more complex but we shall deal with this in the next chapter.

Naturally, you will avoid meat or poultry stock in the soup, or those little bits of ham, and there is no way you are going to slip in shrimps or tuna fish in salad if you are catering for a true vegetarian.

With the desserts do watch out for things like gelatine which is unacceptable as it is made from calves hooves. You can use Agar Agar instead. Most vegetarians will not eat battery produced eggs. Some will eat free-range. When in doubt, leave them out. If you have the opportunity of asking them that's a good idea but you may not always get that chance.

Should you be making a quiche or a cheesecake, your end product will normally be more appreciated if it has wholemeal and organic ingredients in the pastry. Naturally, any cheese should be vegetarian cheese (that is, animal rennet free). Avoid any unacceptable ingredients in the quiche filling, such as non-vegetarian cheese or ham/bacon.

Chapter Four

CATERING FOR THE VEGAN DIET

WHY VEGAN?

"What on earth do they eat?" If I had as many pounds for the number of times I've heard that, or similar, about people on a vegan diet I would be a very rich person. The remarkable thing is they eat very well indeed. When I go to a vegan house for dinner, I know I will have a banquet. I will cover this subject fully in this chapter but first it is important to have some background of the diet to help you understand the best way to cater for a vegan.

The vegan diet consists solely of foods produced from plants, which are of course our primary food source. To a large extent 'veganism' is a way of life rather than just a diet. However, it excludes foods such as meat, fish or dairy products, which are secondary in the food chain. People often progress naturally from vegetarianism to veganism for one, or more, of the following four reasons:

1. Animal Rights

Vegans believe that we should cease contributing to the exploitation and cruelty suffered by animals which are reared for their flesh, skins and other products. This reason is particularly relevant now that such suffering has become an intrinsic part of modern factory farming methods, especially in the vast broiler chicken industry. Few people can walk through a battery unit or intensive pig farm or, even more relevant, the veal calf unit where the surplus calves are removed from their mother at the dairy milk production unit and kept in terrible conditions, without feeling some empathy with vegan attitudes. It is this latter activity that often causes people to avoid dairy products.

2.   Nutritional Benefits

Vegan food has nutritional benefits because naturally balanced whole (unrefined) food is low on fats and cholesterol and not over-rich in protein.   Furthermore, plant food does not contain the various chemicals that are fed to animals to make their flesh tender and to help them gain weight rapidly, and thereby to ensure the best possible return for the money invested in them.

3.   Better Land Use

The vegan diet contributes to the better use of the land available for growing food. Stock rearing is an extravagant and ecologically unsound way of using land – why grow grain to feed a cow, then eat the cow? Why not just eat the grain in the first place? Most of the world's food problems could be alleviated if land now devoted to stock rearing was turned over to plant cultivation.

4.   A Way of Life

For most vegans their aim of avoiding exploitation of animals affects every aspect of their lifestyle. Vegans do not go in for hide furniture, feather duvets or leather shoes. They hold strong, carefully thought out views and anyone catering for a vegan should respect them.

FORBIDDEN FOODS

A great deal of what I have said in Chapter 3 about vegetarians applies to vegans too. But here are some of the main products to avoid, apart from the obvious meat, fish, eggs and dairy products:

Anything containing gelatine (because it is made from calves' hooves).

Cheese, even a sprinkling on pasta, unless it is vegan cheese (for example, cheese made from soya).

Commercial cakes and biscuits, unless the ingredients panel shows clearly that they contain no eggs or animal fats or egg/milk derivatives such as whey, lactose, lactic acid, casein and albumen.

Cream or custard, UNLESS you use one of the vegan milks like soya which are made entirely from plant products and the custard is egg-free.

Honey (because that is a secondary food source - think about it) although some vegans will eat honey.

Ice Cream unless it is 'vegan' (because most ice creams and sorbets contain animal fats, dairy products, or both: if in doubt read the ingredients panel). There are plenty of 'non-dairy' ice creams about.

Margarines and other spreads unless they are made entirely from vegetable products (see Buyer's Guide).

Mayonnaise, sorbet or mousse (because they contain eggs). Vegan mayonnaise is available.

Pastry made with animal fats or dairy products (use vegetable margarine and do not glaze the pastry with egg or milk).

Worcester Sauce which contains anchovies. (There is a vegan Worcester Sauce.)

Wine or beer, which should be checked to see that animal products have not been used for refining – if in doubt, ask your guest, or leave it out.

Do remember to read product labels for ingredients.

VEGAN VARIETY
Vegan food is often cheap and always wholesome, but it is NOT just a matter of salad. At first glance a diet without meat, fish, butter, eggs, cheese, honey or dairy products may seem impossibly restrictive. It isn't. There are countless delicious pulses, nuts, grains, fruits and vegetables just waiting to be transformed into wonderful dishes.

Don't get hung up on pulses because you may think they take a long time to prepare. They only take a few seconds to drop into water for soaking and if they need to soak for 24 hours you don't have to stand and watch them! The time you actually spend is minutes. Not all pulses have to be soaked for long periods. Red lentils can be prepared from scratch in a few minutes.

You will find some excellent recipes for vegans in our recipe section.

Here, are a few examples of starters and savouries, all quite suitable for non-vegans too:

Guacamole Soup, Vegetable Soup, Tomato Soup
Crudités with Avocado Dip
Vegetable and Bean Biryani
Vegan Pilaff
Vegetable and Nut Pie (variety of recipes)
Ratatouille
Stuffed Aubergines
See also the Recipe section.
For dessert, any fruit pie or crumble is acceptable provided the crust is OK (see above), and fruit salads, fritters (fried in vegetable oil) and purées are a great success.

You may not be an expert on the vegan diet - not in great detail anyway, but this chapter should be enough to avoid the pitfalls I have listed above.

BE SCRUPULOUS

Remember what has been written in Chapter 3 about contamination. For vegans, you have to add dairy products, eggs and honey to the list. Remember some vegans eat honey, but it is best to check or leave it out. You will not use the same utensils for non-vegan and vegan food without washing them in between. Better to use separate utensils. With current salmonella and listeria these precautions make sound sense anyway.

Some strict vegans will eat out only at vegan restaurants that they trust. Here they can be sure that a spoon that has just served meat will not be used for their lentils. But many vegans enjoy eating out with non-vegan friends, and others have to go into hospital. They then have to trust the establishment to play fair with them.

And you must play fair. A little reassurance may be needed on your part. You may need, for example, to give a clear assurance that no meat stock has been near your vegetable soup, and that you are well aware of the need to use vegetable margarine for your pastry. Both your vegan guests and their companions will appreciate your concern and thoughtfulness.

WHOLEFOOD FOR PREFERENCE

It is also worth remembering that those who have chosen a vegan diet often prefer wholefood ingredients to refined ones. But don't be surprised if they are not as interested in the health aspect of their diet as perhaps they should be. It is a good idea, however, to use wholefood flour and bread, brown rice, organically grown vegetables, etc., for your vegan meals. They will taste far better anyway. Many non-vegans and non-vegetarians have adopted a wholefood approach to their diets, and a reputation for delicious wholefood dishes will win you many friends.

YOUR GOLDEN RULES FOR PLEASING YOUR VEGAN GUESTS

1. Play fair with your vegan guests and keep 'contaminated' products and utensils away from their food at all times.
2. Avoid forbidden foods at all stages of food preparation.
3. When catering for vegans within a group of assorted diners, do not alter the rest of the meal or only offer salad unless this is being offered to everyone in the party. Many vegans want to blend in with the catering arrangements and not be highlighted in public.
4. Replace the meat or fish portion with an acceptable vegan "savoury". It may sound crazy to have to say so often but vegans DO eat the same supporting vegetables as non-vegans!!
5. However proud you are of your handiwork, be unobtrusive about the vegan savouries you serve. Your care is appreciated but nobody likes to feel over-fussed in company.

Finally, although I have gone into a fair amount of detail on the vegan diet, it really need not be a problem. If you are a home cook who prides yourself on ONLY providing 'savouries' that are mixed carefully from your own selected ingredients, you may still find it worthwhile (sensible) to use ready-mixed dry, frozen, or chilled packs in the transitional period. Today these are so good that your guests will not suffer, but in fact will gain, if the end result is that you are more relaxed and do not need notice or a long time in preparation.

Dry packs have a long shelf life, are not expensive and can always be used as a base savoury to receive your own extra ingredients to satisfy your creative needs! And remember, you don't have to be a vegan to enjoy meals prepared for that diet. No kitchen need therefore be without a vegan dry, or frozen pack for the unexpected guest and few take more than 15 minutes to prepare. If you do make up a vegan dish from scratch then do remember to make enough for more than one portion and place the rest into individual portions in the freezer for quick use next time.

Chapter Five

ALLERGIES

No-one catering for the special diets of strangers would be expected to know which products can cause problems due to allergies. Allergies are often very complex. For example, a very common problem is with dairy products, including milk, cheese, butter, cream, etc. and all manufactured items which contain these. However, some people are only allergic to milk.

Most people with a diet problem due to allergies know what they can and cannot eat. It is up to you, as the person responsible for the preparation of the meal, to ensure these products, once known to you, are not included.

As this chapter will explain, only a minute amount is necessary to trigger off the allergic reaction. This puts a heavy responsibility on the person providing the meal but, as long as simple precautions are taken, no difficulties should arise. For ease of writing I will refer to the person receiving the meal as the 'guest'. I appreciate it could be a member of the family, or in the case of a hotel a customer or a nursing home a patient.

Do put one thought out of your head – the allergy is NOT just in the mind of your guest. Kill that thought now, otherwise you may be tempted to be careless and think that a little will not matter, providing your guest does not know. Even if there was the possibility, on rare occasions, for the guest to react to something because they thought it would affect them, it's really not worth the risk.

Read the whole of this section carefully and you will have no doubts at the end on how to cope with this difficult diet problem.

While we do not want to go too deeply into the health aspect of diets, it is still important to have a grasp of the basic needs of someone with an allergy in order to be able to cope with food preparation. Gwynne H. Davies, N.D., MNTOS, is a Clinical Ecologist who runs a clinic in Somerset which deals with all types of allergies. He provides all his patients with a little booklet on the subject of allergies. With his consent I intend to take some extracts from that booklet.

His booklet is called 'Allergy Sufferers Guide Through The Jungle' and, as you read some of his comments, you will soon see why. He particularly draws attention to the fact that most people with an allergy can cope at home with a carefully selected store cupboard, but points out the problems of eating out, whether at a hotel, restaurant, hospital or at a dinner party.

Quoting directly from his booklet, Mr. Davies states, 'I have heard it said by many patients........ "but I only had a little and surely that could not do me any harm?" Mr. Davies tells his patient "You will now be aware that, when you are tested, we use one millilitre of substance to obtain a reaction, a minute amount but devastating in effect. Do not let the most well meaning of people 'con' you into having something you should not by suggesting... 'oh! go on. A little won't hurt you'. They are not the ones who have to suffer the skin reaction, the gut reaction, the headache, the asthma attack or the streaming nose. They may mean well but do not listen. Of course eating out or having dinner out with friends is a problem, but you must treat it as a challenge - an obstacle course – but one that has to be accepted and objectively dealt with".

The following are true reactions reported to Mr. Davies by his patients and are produced here as he writes on the subject.

'The lady suffered with migraine headaches for seventeen years. After one visit they disappeared and she accepted an invitation to a dinner party. While eating the dessert she suspected the taste of citrus, to which she was allergic. On questioning, the hostess realised with horror that she had used lemon in the dish of apples that were soaking to prevent blackening. Within half an hour that patient had a severe migraine reaction and was ill for two days.

A young lad had asthma and eczema. After treatment it cleared and for fourteen months he was fine. His parents took him to Cornwall on holiday but were delayed in traffic so that, on arrival in St. Austell, there was no 100% wholemeal bread to be found. He was allergic to the chemicals and additives in white flour so they purchased what they thought was the next best thing, a granary loaf. He consumed one slice for his tea; two hours later he was in an oxygen tent in the local hospital'. (NOTE: Changes to white loaves are detailed later in this chapter.)

'A man had severe arthritic reactions with acute pain and severe swelling of joints. After one week on a dairy-free diet these disappeared and he felt fine for many months. One day, quite without thinking, he ate something which contained milk, to which he was allergic. In one hour he was in severe pain and his wrists swelled to enormous proportions. This will indicate to you how necessary it is to eliminate the 'trigger' foods completely.

I will come to the important task of guiding you through the JUNGLE in a moment but let us first go through some of the most common mistakes made by patients, either through misunderstanding or carelessness, or even my inability to emphasise the pitfalls enough.

MILK.

You are allergic to cows milk. Oh! that is easy, you think. I will avoid things with milk in. It really is not that simple, for milk is in various forms which are listed below and lurk in the most unlikely places. Who would think, for one moment, that by eating a wine gum you were ingesting milk – not many I would think but there it is – Lactic Acid.

"Oh! well, if I can't have milk I will have margarine" – you cannot and must not eat normal margarine for most contain whey or lactose or lactic acid. Do not despair, you will not have to eat dry bread because there are vegetarian or kosher margarines to choose from. One kosher margarine is called TOMOR. The vegetarian margarines include VITAQUELLE, VITASIEG, GRANOSE, PURE, SUMA AND VITELMA. Tesco and Sainsbury also sell Dairy Free Margarine.

"If I am allergic to milk, does that mean that I am automatically allergic to all milk products?"

No, due to enzymatic changes that take place, one can be allergic to one but not necessarily all.

CHEESE.

Invariably, it is the rennet in cheese that causes the problem. This automatically precludes cream cheese, soft cheeses such as Brie, Camembert, etc. An expensive treat occasionally is Roquefort but the most commonly used alternative is an ANIMAL RENNET FREE cheese obtainable from most health shops and supermarkets. Do ask for it, as it is kept in the cooler.'

GOAT'S, SHEEP AND SOYA MILK.

Mr. Davies continues, 'Goat's milk is the most popular of alternatives and the one I prefer. Depending on the dietary habits, etc. of a particular herd, you may occasionally obtain milk that is "goaty" or separates very easily. This is not applicable to all goat's milk. Shop around, for a good goat's milk is delicious and nutritious.

SOYA milk is another alternative. SHEEP milk watered down half and half is also delicious.

DANGER!!! BEWARE!!! If you have a milk allergy, avoid the following: LACTOSE. LACTIC ACID, CASEIN, WHEY, SKIMMED MILK.

The undermentioned products can, and frequently do, contain milk in one form or another:-

Baking powder, biscuits, bakers bread, bavarian cream, blancmange, salad dressings, butter, buttermilk, butter sauces, cakes, chocolates, chocolate or cocoa drinks or mixtures, cream, creamed foods, cream sauces, curds, custards, doughnuts, eggs (scrambled) and escalloped dishes.

Foods prepared au gratin, foods fried in butter (fish, poultry, beef, pork), flour mixtures, fritters, gravies, hamburgers, hash, hard sauces, ice creams, mashed potato, malted milk, Ovaltine, meat loaf, cooked sausages, milk chocolate, milk in all forms, omelettes, some margarines, pie crust made with milk products, popcorn. Prepared food mixes for biscuits, cakes, doughnuts, muffins, pancakes, pie crust, waffles and puddings. Rarebits, salad dressings, sherbets, souffles, soups, sweets, junket. This list is a guide. Manufacturers do change the contents of their products frequently, so be on your guard and do not relax your vigilance.'

Remember that in these extracts Mr. Davies is writing for his patients, but you may find it of interest. He goes on:

'You will be delighted to know that since April, 1992, additives and preservatives have been banned in white flour to conform to EC regulations. On the packet of flour it should state "UNBLEACHED WHITE FLOUR - NO ARTIFICIAL ADDITIVES", the stabiliser used is L Ascorbic acid which is Vitamin C and is safe. Some of you, particularly arthritics, may find difficulty in ingesting wholemeal flour successfully, creating pain and suffering. This is due to the difficulty of the gut in digesting the bran and husk in wholemeal and produces phytic acid.'

This chapter has mainly been devoted to a background on food allergies and some of the hidden problems in trying to avoid some items. However, as mentioned at the start of this chapter, you are not expected to go too deeply into allergies, but you will find a background knowledge is helpful when catering for special diets. You should be aware that products change and you should seek professional advice before embarking on any allergy diet.

For more reading on the subject, you can purchase Gwynne Davies's book 'Overcoming Food Allergies' from Ashgrove Press, 19 Circus Place, Bath, Avon, BA1 2PW.

Chapter Six

OTHER DIETS

Included in this chapter: *CANDIDA ALBICANS * THE COELIAC (GLUTEN-FREE) * DIABETICS * FASTING * THE HAY SYSTEM * HIGH FIBRE * HINDU * KOSHER * MUSLIMS * RAW FOOD * SLIMMING*

As with the other sections of this book, extracts on selected diets from different people and organisations have been included to simply give an overview. These have been put together as points of reference, although recognising that with diets and nutrition there is, and may always be, a wide divergence between one expert and another. For convenience these diets have been listed under Medical and Religion.

Any diet not included does not mean it is of less importance than those included. I have selected examples in order to provide a broad view of some of the diets you may find yourself catering for. See also useful contacts and further reading at the back of this book.

It is not the purpose of this book to say what is the correct diet or best for your guest. That is really up to the individual. The purpose of this book is to help you to cope with the special diets of people who come to you. With that in mind, here are some diets which may come your way. It is again emphasised that you are not expected to become an expert on all diets unless there is some special reason for this, but simply to have an understanding in broad terms. Information is, therefore, essentially brief and should be supplemented with specialist information if required for individual cases.

MEDICAL & GENERAL DIETS

For some people, diet is not a matter of conscience, but of necessity. If they do not follow certain rules, they will suffer for it. Here are some examples of "medical" diets and their implications for the 'provider'. (Please refer to Chapter One for the objectives of this book.)

DIETS FOR CANDIDA ALBICANS

Candida Albicans has become well known over recent years. Let us look at what it is. It is when the body produces too much yeast. A type of yeast infection. Candida is claimed to be with us from soon after birth. It is a parasite, a yeast-like organism which, in the infective phase, produces a condition called 'thrush' (candidiasis) that often gives inflammation of the mucous membranes of the mouth of an infant and, sometimes, adults. One of the most common effects of chronic 'Candida' infection is in recurring vaginal infections or cystitis. There are plenty of books on Candida and these are included in the reference index. Meanwhile, here is a typical diet for someone wishing to bring the yeast infection under control. It is important to note, however, that no one should embark on this diet without proper advice from a skilled practitioner.

Items to AVOID

Sugars, sucrose, honeys, sweeteners, fructose, glucose, malt, syrups, molasses, fruit and fruit juice (for first two months of treatment), dried fruit, yoghurts (while taking Acidophilus-type products), fungus-forming foods (mushrooms, unfresh nuts), dairy products (milk, cheese, butter, etc.), smoked fish and smoked meats, yeasts (breads, yeast spreads, etc.), fermented foods (soya sauce, miso, beer, etc.), alcoholic beverages, monosodium glutamate, preservatives, frozen peas, peanuts and pistachios, foods you are allergic to, birth control pills, gluten – rye, wheat, oats, barley.

Green Farm Nutrition Centre, in its article on Candida gives a similar list plus the following:-

Maltose, glycogen, mannital, sorbital galactose, monosaccharides, poly-saccharides, date sugar, sweets and chocolate, sweet biscuits and cakes, puddings and desserts, maple, date and rice syrup, soft drinks, tonic water, milkshakes (sugar foods). Always check canned, packaged or ready prepared meals for added sugars or yeast. Pickles, relishes, vinegar, raised pastries, any sauce containing vinegar, mustard, horseradish, mayonnaise, tamari, salad dressing, and anything covered in breadcrumbs. Buttermilk, sour cream, cottage cheese, truffles, sour milk products, cheese dressings, cream cheese.

Antibiotics – dairy products or poultry, eggs and meat often contain residues of antibiotics, unless purchased from an organic supplier. Also suspect are tea, coffee, melons, ready sprouted grains, foods containing malt and un-fresh fruit.

Permitted Foods
Shellfish, unsmoked fish, antibiotic and steroid-free meat and chicken, vegetables – especially cooked broccoli, cauliflower, swede, cabbage family, eggs, garlic, fresh vegetable juice – especially carrot, celery and beet, olive oil - rich in oleic acid which inhibits candida, linseed oil – rich in linoleic acid, psyllium husks (for dietary fibre), filtered water and mineral water, millet, rice, pulses.

RAW FOOD DIET
This may need a little explanation. It is claimed to have a dramatic effect on people with so called incurable illnesses like cancer. Apart from the benefits to those with health problems, it is also claimed to be excellent in preventing illnesses such as heart attacks and bowel conditions. Leslie and Susannah Kenton have highlighted the benefits of this with their book 'RAW ENERGY'.

The basis of the diet is to ensure that 75% of foods are eaten raw. This produces not only incredible results in curing illness, but also gives extra energy for those who already feel well! It is also claimed to reverse bodily degeneration and thereby retard the rate at which you age. The diet can be very interesting, so read any of the books on the subject and ensure your guests can have really exciting meals with 75% raw food.

THE HAY SYSTEM DIET
The Hay System consists of five rules.
1.   Starches and sugars should not be eaten with proteins and acid fruits at the same meal.

2.   Vegetables, salads and fruits should form the major part of the diet.
3.   Proteins, starches and fats should be eaten in small quantities only.
4.   Only whole grain and unprocessed starches should be used and all refined processed foods are prohibited - in particular, white flour and sugar and all foods made with them, and highly processed fats such as margarine.
5.   Intervals of at least four hours should elapse between meals of different character.

Many famous people have used this diet when they claim other, more orthodox methods, have failed to resolve a medical or energy problem. Sir John Mills was invalided out of the Army in 1942 with a duodenal ulcer. Hospital treatment with normal diet of rice puddings, mashed potatoes, etc. plus medical help only seemed to make matters worse. His sister suggested the Hay Diet and, with the support of his wife Mary, he followed this diet and has never looked back. This also enabled him to cope with work he would not have been able to handle without this diet. Within six weeks of commencement he started work on a film and recently wrote that, over forty years later, he was playing in eight shows a week which meant it was essential to be really fit.

Dr. William Hay was born in the USA in 1866. For sixteen years he practised medicine 'according to the best light of his time' with considerable surgery. His own health failed at the end of this period and he received a warning from fellow doctors to put his own affairs in order. He decided to eat 'fundamentally', eating only such foods as he believed were intended by Nature as food for man. He took them in natural form and in quantities no greater than seemed necessary for his need! To the astonishment of his doctors his symptoms gradually disappeared and, in three months, he felt fitter and stronger than he had done in years.

For the next four years he devoted his time to treating patients on these same dietary lines. Like so many good 'pioneers' he claimed 'he had not discovered anything new, but simply used the knowledge already made public by others and then consolidated it with his own input of common sense'. He emphasised that the 'system' only removed the obstacles in the way of

Nature's own healing powers. Since then his ideas have been supported by many foremost medical authorities.

The basis of the Hay Diet is not to mix starch foods with proteins.

Fortunately, there is a long list of 'neutral foods' and this includes most vegetables (excluding potatoes or Jerusalem artichokes - tomatoes may also be difficult), so you can use any of these with either starch or protein products. The table of compatible foods sets the scene. All you have to do is select your products to make your guest happy and well.

One final point, on this brief resume, is the misunderstanding about the classification of PROTEINS and CARBOHYDRATES.

Proteins are those that are concentrated (i.e. 20% or more). Normally these are animal proteins like meat, fish, cheese, poultry, eggs, fresh milk, etc.

Carbohydrates are also those concentrated with 20% or more starches, such as grains, bread, cereals, potatoes and sugars. Difficult products are mature, or dried, legumes - peas, beans, lentils and peanuts, which contain too high a percentage of both protein and starch to be compatible in themselves but are fine 'sprouted'.

FASTING

To fast means, simply, not eating. To most people, however, it includes drinks suited to the person and the fast. Many people fast one day each week in order to improve their health. These short fasts of one, two or three days allow one cup (or just less) every three or four hours of a suitable liquid. This could be a teaspoon of honey with hot water or just a herb tea. Never should the liquid be ordinary tea or coffee and certainly not milk.

Those people on a fast should have consulted a doctor or nutritionist first, if possible, and this is particularly important if the person is old, sick or an expectant mother or has diabetes or stomach ulcers. Some of your guests may be on a semi-fast and take some raw food or simply cut out carbohydrates, proteins and sugar for the day, or however long intended.

After fasting, the guest should not overload their digestive system, so it is important they restart with small meals that are especially low in protein.

There are some excellent books on fasting and, if you are interested, ask at your local health food shop or check our abridged reference list. Fasting is not generally recommended for young women in their teens, as this could encourage anorexia nervosa.

HIGH FIBRE DIET

If you have to cope with someone on a high fibre diet you can usually rely on them, or their medical advisor, for guidance, as each person is different in their requirements. Lack of fibre in the diet is often blamed for problems of cancer, diverticulitis, colitis and heart disease. Constipation is considered by many experts as one of the causes of these and other diseases.

High bran cereals and wholewheat bread are recommended, plus plenty of fresh vegetables and fruit every day.

CATERING FOR SLIMMERS

Without doubt diets for slimmers have to be at the top of the list as far as everyday demand is concerned. However, for those catering for someone on a slimming diet it's no big deal, providing they understand what the diet entails. There are so many different diets, all undertaken with weight loss in mind, that it is impossible to put down all the various restrictions. However, most slimmers are grateful for our concern and glad to discuss their needs.

Here are the commonest forms of slimming and the points to remember about each one.

Low Calorie

A calorie is a unit of energy. All food contains calories, because all food provides energy. Our energy needs depend on age and lifestyles: an active teenager requires many more calories per day than a sedentary middle-aged person. In that sense, all food is fattening: if you consume more calories than you need, they are stored as fat. On the other hand, if you eat fewer calories than the body needs, you will lose weight because your body has to draw on its own reserves of fat to meet its energy needs. A daily limit of 1,000 to 1,500 calories, depending on your age and lifestyle, will usually ensure a steady weight loss.

Some foods, such as butter and chocolate, contain a great many calories per serving. Others, such as mushrooms and cucumber, contain very few. In theory people who are counting calories could use up their whole day's allowance on three Mars bars, or instead consume several bucketfuls of lettuce. The calorific value would be the same. Obviously neither diet would be healthy or sensible. The aim is to take in a healthy and balanced diet within the calorie limit allowed.

Most calorie counters carry a calorie chart in their pocket or in their head! Fats, milk, cheese, nuts, paté, fatty meats and sugary foods such as dried fruit, sweets and cakes are all high in calories, as are many packaged and processed foods. Bread, rice, cereals, pasta and potatoes are not in themselves very high in calories, but are often eaten in conjunction with fats (bread and butter, fried potatoes, fried rice), which increase their calorific value alarmingly. Likewise, rich gravies and sauces add large numbers of calories to otherwise acceptable fish, lean meat, pasta and eggs.

Green vegetables and most fruits and salads are low in calories. As soon as sauces, dressings, sugar, cream, etc. are added, however, their calorific value rockets.

'Small is beautiful' is a good rule when catering for calorie counters. So is 'toujours la presentation'. Try to make your small, calorie controlled meals look as attractive as possible.

CATERING FOR DIABETICS

Many people are anxious faced with the prospect of catering for someone with diabetes. The British Diabetic Association offers the following guidelines:-

"In actual fact the diet recommended for diabetes is just a healthy diet, similar to the type of diet we should all be eating. People with diabetes should:-

Increase their fibre intake by eating more wholemeal bread, wholegrain cereals, brown rice and pasta, pulses (peas, beans), fruit and vegetables.

Decrease their fat intake by cutting down on fried foods, using low-fat dairy products, i.e. skimmed or semi-skimmed milk and by restricting their intake of fatty foods such as pastries, fatty meats, chips and salad dressings.

Cut down on the amount of sugar and sugary foods they eat. It is important to note that many savoury products such as tinned vegetables, soups and sauces contain sugar. However, the amount of sugar in savoury foods is small and would not effect diabetes control.

Artificial sweeteners such as Sweetex, Canderel and Hermesetas are useful for sweetening drinks, cereals and puddings. For baked goods, the BDA recommend that ordinary sugar be used but in reduced amounts. Home Baking recipes can be obtained from the British Diabetic Association.

Diabetic foods such as sweets, cakes and chocolate are not a necessary part of the diet.

People with diabetes are able to drink alcohol (unless, of course, they have been advised to avoid it for another medical reason). Like everything else, alcohol should be taken in moderation. Special low sugar beers and diabetic wines are not necessary and are often higher in alcohol. Ordinary beers, lagers and wines are perfectly acceptable although the dry-medium varieties of wine are preferable to the sweet ones. It is a good idea to have a selection of low calorie mixers and sugar-free non-alcoholic drinks available too.

Regular meals will be helpful, especially for those on insulin. In addition, if your guest knows what times (approximately) you hope to serve meals, it will help them co-ordinate their insulin injections with meal times.

Some people, again especially those on insulin, are advised to eat a certain amount of carbohydrate (i.e. bread, potatoes, pasta, rice) at each meal. Your guest will know how much carbohydrate he will require, so make sure you have some source of carbohydrate at each meal and then let them help themselves.

Don't panic – you will not upset your guest's diabetes control by serving a high fat/high sugar menu. There are no bad foods – just bad diets. Remember, it is the day-to-day diet which is important and the occasional treat does no-one any harm. Your guest may, therefore, prefer to take the gooey dessert like everyone else!

A discreet chat with your guest before they arrive may give you some idea of their particular diet and of the foods they may prefer not to eat. Most people with diabetes are very competent dealing with their diet and diabetes and you will probably realise that there wasn't anything to worry about after all.

If you require any further information, please contact the Diet Information Service.

The British Diabetic Association, 10, Queen Anne Street, LONDON. W1M 0BD.

THE COELIAC (GLUTEN-FREE) DIET

Gluten is found in cereals such as wheat, rye, oats and barley. As flour is made from wheat, all baked foods such as bread, cakes and biscuits will normally contain gluten and must therefore be avoided by anyone on a gluten-free diet.

A gluten-free diet excludes the following:
Bread, buns, biscuits, cakes, pastry, batters and any recipe which uses flour or breadcrumbs. Spaghetti, macaroni, noodles or other pasta. Ryvita, Vitaweat, Energen Rolls and other starch-reduced products. Weetabix, Puffed Wheat, Shredded Wheat and other wheat cereals. Semolina, sauces and gravies thickened with flour. (Special gluten-free bread, flour, biscuits and pasta are available).

A list of gluten-free manufactured or processed foods can be obtained from the Coeliac Society. It is important to keep it updated as manufacturers change their recipes from time to time.

Foods which are safe to include:
Fresh meat, frozen unprocessed meat, chicken, liver, kidney, bacon, ham (without breadcrumb coating). Fresh fish: frozen uncoated fish, smoked fish, fish tinned in oil. Eggs, milk (fresh, dried or tinned), cream (fresh or tinned). Vegetables and salads (fresh, frozen or tinned in brine). Fruit of all kinds and fruit juices. Nuts. Butter, margarine, cooking oils, lard dripping. Rice, sago, tapioca, arrowroot, pure cornflour, jellies. Cornflakes, Rice Crispies. Ricicles. Sugar, jam, honey, syrup, marmalade, boiled sweets. Chocolate (plain or milk but without biscuit fillings). Tea, coffee, fruit squash, fizzy drinks, Bovril, Marmite, pure cocoa. Salt, pure pepper, vinegar, herbs, spices, essences.

Any food listed in the Coeliac Society's gluten-free list.

SUGGESTED MEALS FOR A GLUTEN-FREE DIET

Breakfast: Cornflakes or Rice Crispies with milk and sugar. Gluten-free bread, toast or Aproten crispbreads with butter and honey, marmalade or Marmite.
Bacon, eggs, tomatoes, mushrooms, fish, ham or cheese, fruit or fruit juices.

Midmorning or other snacks: Home-made gluten-free cakes or pastries or chocolate Krispies. "Rite-Diet" or home-made gluten-free snacks biscuits. Chocolate, cheese with an apple or a gluten-free scone.

Hot Meals: Roast, stewed or grilled meat (with cornflour gravy); grilled, poached or fried fish (coated with gluten-free crumbs, batter or crushed cornflakes); omelette, poached fried or scrambled eggs; cauliflower cheese (using cornflour to make the sauce); potatoes cooked in any of the normal ways; any vegetables, fresh or tinned in salt and water; tinned or stewed fruit with cream or gluten-free custard; pastry or crumble made with gluten-free flour; jellies, ice-cream (see List for safe varieties); milk puddings (rice, sago, tapioca, NOT semolina).

Cold or packed meals: Cold meats, hard boiled eggs, cheese, tinned fish in oil. Homemade gluten-free pies or pasties with meat or cheese and egg or vegetable fillings.
Any salad vegetable (plain or dressed with real mayonnaise or oil and vinegar dressing).
Rice salads or potato salads.
Gluten-free bread and butter.
Fresh fruit, gluten-free cakes or biscuits or homemade jam tarts or meringues.

Beverages: Tea, coffee, Bovril, Marmite, cocoa, gluten-free brands or drinking chocolate.
Fruit squashes, PLJ, tomato juice, Ribena, Delrosa, 'baby' orange juice, all kinds of pure fruit juices. Fizzy lemonades, Coca Cola, Pepsi Cola, Lucozade.

A booklet is available from the Coeliac Society for medically diagnosed coeliacs which lists suitable manufacturers' products Contact the Coeliac Society of the UK, P. O. Box 220, High Wycombe, Bucks. HP11 2HY.

DIET AND RELIGION

Most of this information is covered under the respective diets. As with all special dietary needs, coping begins with the person accepting a dinner invitation. Jews and Muslims are the most obvious examples nowadays, although until quite recently it was usual to serve meatless dishes on Fridays for the benefit of Roman Catholics, for whom Friday was a fast day. Many Catholics do still choose to abstain from meat on Fridays.

Diets may be Jewish, Muslim, Hindu or any religion that requires special attention. You will naturally want to make sure that everyone concerned in preparing and serving the meal is aware of the implications of your guest's diet to avoid offence.

Be Scrupulous

For these people, diet is part of their religion and their religion is part of their lifestyle. Outside the home, they rely on the provider of their food to play fair with them. Check the ingredients to make sure no unacceptable foods are included in the meal.

HINDU FOOD

Some brief notes on the background of diets requested for religious reasons. Hinduism is founded on reverence for life. Because it is against their religion to kill any form of life, most Hindus are either vegetarian or vegan. To cater for Hindu guests, turn straight to Chapters 3 and 4.

KOSHER FOOD

Kosher is Hebrew for 'lawful' or 'proper'. The basis is the Old Testament. Jews vary in the strictness of their adherence to the rules. Meat from any animal without cloven hooves should be OK.

The following are unacceptable: pork or horse meat and any products containing such meat – eg bacon, sausages, salami, hot dogs, lard, paté, etc.

Blood (rare steak, black puddings, etc.)

Fish and seafood without fins and scales - ie crabs, lobsters, scallops, scampi, prawns, mussels, oysters, etc.

Meat that has not been ritually slaughtered by a Kosher butcher.

Towns where there is a sizeable Jewish community are likely to have at least one butcher who sells Kosher meat. Fish, egg and vegetable dishes are usually acceptable.

In addition, flesh and milk products must not be consumed at the same meal. In a kosher kitchen, separate utensils are used for preparing, serving and washing up the two food categories. *This cuts out the following:*

Creamy sauces and soups, etc. with meat, fish or chicken (you could use kosher margarine and soya milk, informing your guest discreetly that this is what you are doing).

Yoghurt as a marinade for meat.

Butter, either for cooking flesh or with bread in conjunction with a meat meal (use beef dripping, vegetable oil or kosher margarine instead). Cheese as a garnish for a meat dish (such as grated cheese on top of a meaty lasagne).

If in doubt, it is still best to ask! Discuss discreetly what is and is not acceptable. Your Jewish guests will appreciate your concern and understanding.

There is now a Jewish Vegetarian Society. Full details are listed in the reference section.

CATERING FOR MUSLIMS

Islamic dietary laws were set out in the Qu'ran. Not all Muslims observe them strictly, but the foods laid down by Muhammad as unacceptable are:- "Foods previously sacrificed to idols", which are unlikely to be much of a problem!

All pork and pork products (pork, bacon, sausages, hot dogs, salami, lard, patés containing pork, etc. Blood (rare steak, black pudding, etc.

Non-halal meat and, therefore, any products containing this meat, eg dripping, meat stock cubes, brawns, 'bought' pastry, patés, salamis, hard margarines, etc. etc.

Halal means 'lawful' and refers to the way in which the animal has been butchered. Kosher meat, which is also ritually butchered, is acceptable. Most towns with a large concentration of Jews and/or Muslims have a Kosher or Halal butcher and you may, given notice, be able to arrange a supply of doctrinally acceptable meat and chicken from there. Unless you have a reliable source of such meat, however, it is best to tell the person so frankly, and offer a fish, egg or vegetarian dish. Your Muslim guests will appreciate your concern and understanding.

No Alcohol
There is one more important restriction: Good Muslims abstain from all alcoholic beverages. This includes those used in the cooking of food; such dishes as coq au vin, even if the chicken is halal are, therefore, unacceptable.

Ramadan
During this month of fasting, no food or drink is taken between sunrise and sunset. Like Lent it is a movable feast, depending on the phases of the moon and, like Lent, it is a month of atonement. Although young children, pregnant women or breast-feeding women and old or sick people are usually excused, other Muslims will usually breakfast (if at all) before the sun is up, then eat or drink nothing until after sunset.

SIKHS
Sikhism started as an offshoot of Islam and became a religion in its own right. Sikhs worship a personal God and each person's diet is a matter of personal choice. You will, therefore, meet vegetarian Sikhs as well as Sikhs who eat meat and fish. No Sikh is likely to eat beef or pork, however, and alcohol is forbidden, but some less devout Sikhs do drink occasionally. If in doubt – ask.

Chapter 7

RECISPES

*I*n the introductory chapters I stated it is not intended that this *publication be used as a recipe book. There are hundreds of* *excellent recipe books available covering every possible diet.*

The recipes and notes in this section are here to show examples of meals that can illustrate the variety available to those readers not used to catering for special diets - and for those who would like to try something different.

Some of the recipes are by Katherine Monbiot, who has been working in the field of therapeutic nutrition for many years. She has also produced a helpful video entitled 'The Gourmet Way to Health' which is available by post and covers a range of meals free from animal ingredients, dairy products, egg, salt, sugar and wheat! There are also fat and gluten-free options. Katherine is available for corporate training, in addition to her work as a dietary therapist. Katherine is not only a vegan herself but also holds the title of the British Women's Arm Wrestling Champion - some diet!

I have also included recipes from Sue Kreitzman's books and these are wonderful for diets that are fat-free. Others are from Barbara Cousins from her book 'Cooking Without'. Barbara is the proprietor of the Natural Healing Clinic in North Manchester. Although she practises other therapies, diet and detoxification are used with all patients as Barbara feels that the way we eat has such a great influence on our health and well-being.

Do not forget the many ready-made meals suitable for virtually every diet available from your local health shop or supermarket. If in doubt, send a large S.A.E. for further information from our Reader Enquiry Service. Details can be found at the back of this book along with a section headed 'Useful Contacts'.

Happy catering. Enjoy the food and enjoy the company of your guest, whatever the diet.

RECIPES BY KATHERINE MONBIOT

Coding	*Vegan, wheat-free, low sodium, low fat. **Vegan, low sodium, gluten-free.
STARTERS	*Walnut tartlets with wild mushrooms and leek goulash with a red pepper sauce. *Courgette and leek mousse with tomato and basil coulis *Pepper, apple and saffron soup
MAIN COURSES	**Sri Lankan curried pumpkin **Stir fried vegetables with mixed rices and satay sauce **Cashew and caper loaf
DESSERTS	Vegan, gluten-free, low fat, low sugar Ice cream sundae *** and low sugar - Tofu cheesecake

RECIPES BY SUE KREITZMAN

STARTER	Creamy parsnip soup - non-fat vegan
MAIN COURSE	Pasta primavera non-fat vegan Cous cous with vegetables – non-fat vegetarian

RECIPES BY BARBARA COUSINS
Wheat, Sugar, Salt, Dairy and Yeast Free. Low Fat*

BREAKFAST	Pear and carob delight Banana and maize cereal
STARTER	Spinach and carrot timbale
MAIN COURSE	Nutty vegetable loaf Broccoli and sweetcorn quiche
SAUCE	Chick pea sauce
DESSERT	Apricot mousse

* Some are fat free but remember that eggs, oil and nuts all contain fat and therefore a recipe is classed as 'low fat' when these are included.

RECIPE FROM THE HOUSE OF THE AUTHOR

A favourite of mine at my home which is vegetarian, vegan and gluten-free. We call it 'Cashew – Tamari loaf.'

RECIPES BY KATHERINE MONBIOT

STARTERS

Walnut tartlets with wild mushroom and leek goulash with a red pepper sauce

Pastry

6oz/170g medium oatmeal
3oz/85g ground walnuts
½ teaspoon ground cumin

1 teaspoon dried thyme
water to mix

Goulash

1 tablespoon extra virgin olive oil
1 clove garlic, crushed
4 medium leeks, thinly sliced
1lb/455g wild mushrooms
    (including oyster + shitake)

a little stock or water
2 tablespoons salt-free tomato
    purée
1 tablespoon paprika
freshly ground black pepper

Red Pepper Sauce

2 large red peppers, roughly
    chopped
2 garlic cloves, roughly chopped
pinch cayenne pepper

$1/4$ pint/140ml water
2 tablespoons extra virgin olive oil
freshly ground black pepper

To Garnish

A few broken, toasted walnuts
1 red pepper, grilled, peeled and cut into strips

Method

Pastry: Mix oatmeal, walnuts and seasonings, Add enough water to form a fairly sticky dough. Press out into tartlet cases. Bake blind 400°F/200°C Mark 6 for approx. 15 mins. till golden.

Goulash: Heat oil with a little water; add garlic and leeks. Sweat for 5 mins. Add sliced mushrooms, starting with the firmest, and sauté till tender, adding a little more water if necessary. Finally add tomato purée, paprika and pepper and heat through. Pour into cooked flan cases and garnish with toasted pepper strips and toasted walnuts. Serve with red pepper sauce.

Red Pepper Sauce: Simmer peppers, garlic and cayenne in water until tender; liquidise, dribbling in the olive oil. Add pepper to taste. Reheat gently if necessary.

Courgette and Leek Mousse with Tomato and Basil Coulis

1 medium leek
1 teaspoon dried tarragon
2 tablespoons lemon juice
black pepper
3 medium courgettes
1 tablespoon extra virgin olive oil
5oz/130g soft silken tofu or plain
soya yoghurt
3 teaspoons agar flakes or 2 teaspoons agar powder
1/4 pint/140ml water or vegetable stock

Coulis
1/2 lb ripe tomatoes
1 clove garlic, crushed
1 tablespoon extra virgin olive oil
2 sprigs fresh basil
little dry marjoram
black pepper

Mousse Method
1. Slice leeks and courgettes and simmer along with the tarragon until the vegetables are tender.
2. Meanwhile put water or stock in a pan and sprinkle on agar flakes. Bring slowly to the boil, stir and simmer for 1 min. Allow to cool slightly.
3. Liquidize tofu or yoghurt, lemon juice, oil, pepper, and coriander together. Add cooked leeks and courgettes, process till smooth. Add agar mixture and whizz once more. Pour the mixture into 6 ramekins or moulds and leave to set in the fridge for at least 1 hour.

Coulis
1. Skin tomatoes by immersing in boiling water for 30 secs. Sieve or chop tomatoes finely.
2. Add torn basil leaves and remaining ingredients, and spoon the coulis onto six serving plates.
3. Turn the mousses out onto the coulis and garnish with a sprig of fresh basil.

Pepper, Apple and Saffron Soup

2 medium onions (chopped)
2 dessert apples, cored (chopped)
pinch saffron
2 large red peppers (chopped)
1 tablespoon mild curry powder
black pepper
1 ½ pints/850ml vegetable stock or water

Method
Place all ingredients except black pepper in a pan and simmer until soft. Liquidize and add pepper to taste. Strain if a smoother soup is required.

MAIN COURSES

**Sri Lankan Curried Pumpkin*

1 medium pumpkin (green skinned are best)

1 small onion, sliced	*1 red chilli*
1 tablespoon extra virgin olive oil	*sprig curry leaves (optional)*
1 stalk lemon grass	*6 lime leaves (from supermarkets*
1/4 teaspoon black pepper	*or Asian stores)*
1/4 teaspoon turmeric	*3/4 pint/420ml thin coconut milk*
1/4 pint/140ml thick coconut milk	*1 teaspoon brown mustard seed*
1/2 teaspoon, ground coriander	*4 cloves garlic, crushed*
1/4 teaspoon ground cumin	*1 tablespoon lime juice*

Method

1. Sweat onion and chilli in oil and a little water. Add curry and lime leaves, lemon grass, pepper and turmeric.

2. Add diced pumpkin (peel only if skin is very tough), and thin coconut milk. Simmer until pumpkin is tender.

3. Mix thick coconut milk with mustard seed and garlic. Add to pumpkin, followed by cumin and coriander. Cook for a few minutes more. Add the lime juice.

This looks good served in a hollowed out and steamed pumpkin shell

Note: Coconut milk is available in tins from Asian supermarkets, but can also be made using either fresh, grated or desiccated coconut, which then needs to be soaked in boiling water, liquidized, and the remaining liquid squeezed out. Creamed coconut, melted in water, could also be used instead of the thick coconut milk.

If a thicker, richer curry is required, 2 tablespoons brown rice flour blended to a smooth paste with ¼ pint water can be added along with the garlic and mustard seed. The mixture should be simmered until thick (adding more water if necessary).

**Stir Fried Vegetables and Mixed Rices and Satay Sauce*

Peanuts are very indigestible and many people prefer not to eat them, so here is the peanut-free alternative:

4 heaped tablespoons desiccated coconut : – soak for 10 mins in 1 pint of boiling water, then strain, to make coconut milk
2 red chillies
1 stalk lemon grass
1" root ginger, peeled and grated   } *liquidize together with*
1 tablespoon lemon juice   *some of the coconut milk*
1 tablespoon apple juice concentrate
4oz/110g each pecan nuts + almonds, toasted and ground

Method
1. Simmer together coconut milk and liquidize spices for 3-4 mins.
2. Add ground nuts, cover and simmer 3 mins more. Add lemon and apple juices.

Serve over stir fried vegetables with mixed rices.

Mixed Rices
4 oz each short grain organic brown rice, wild rice and brown basmati
2 tablespoons desiccated coconut
1 bunch fresh thyme
1 strip lime rind

Method
Wash the rices and place in pan with twice their volume of water. Add remaining ingredients, cover, bring to the boil, then turn down very low and leave for 40 mins until all the liquid is absorbed.

A VEGGIE DIET THAT SUITS PEOPLE WITH DIABETES

This colourful photograph is from 'The Vegetarian and Diabetes' booklet, published by the British Diabetic Association. Priced at £1.99 it has been written in conjunction with the Vegetarian Society and offers helpful advice and fifty delicious recipes.

As the picture clearly illustrates, these recipes can be very attractive and enjoyed by everyone, whether they have diabetes or not.

**Cashew and Caper Loaf

1 large onion, diced
6 peppercorns
1 heaped tablespoon cornflour
8oz/250g millet, cooked
grated nutmeg
pepper

2 bay leaves
1/2 pint/280ml unsweetened soya milk
6oz/170g cashew nuts, ground
2oz/65g capers, soaked in fresh
    water, then drained

Method

1. Put soya milk in a pan with the onion, bay leaf and peppercorns. Bring to the boil and leave covered for ten minutes.
2. Strain off the soya milk, discarding the bay leaves and peppercorns, but keeping the onion.
3. Mix the cornflour with enough soya milk to make a smooth paste and add to remaining soya milk in a pan; bring to boil and simmer till thick.
4. Add the resulting sauce to the millet along with the onion, cashews and seasonings. Gently fold in the capers. Place in greased loaf tin and bake 350°F/180°C Mark 5 for approx 40 mins till firm and golden. Serve with a robust tomato sauce.

DESSERTS

Ice Cream Sundae
(Vegan, gluten-free, low fat, low sugar)

I have never met anybody who doesn't instantly fall in love with this ultra healthy ice-cream, and it often takes some convincing to reassure people that it is not full of all sorts of "naughties"!

6 ripe bananas, peeled, sliced and frozen
8oz red fruit (strawberries, raspberries, blackberries, etc.) cleaned and
    frozen
8oz ripe mango flesh, diced and frozen
soya milk
2 tablespoons sugar-free cherry jam   2 tablespoons arrowroot
1/2 pint/280ml water

To decorate: toasted flaked almonds, whole strawberries, lime slices

Sauce

Heat together the jam and water. Mix the arrowroot with a little extra water to make a smooth paste. Add to the jam mixture in the pan and simmer until thickened. Allow to cool before spooning into the bottom of 6 champagne flutes or sundae glasses.

Ice Cream

You will need to work fast with this as it melts quickly and cannot be refrozen.

Place half the frozen bananas in a food processor along with the frozen red fruit and just enough soya milk to process easily. Whizz until very smooth. Tip into a bowl and return to freezer to keep cool whilst you do the same with the remaining bananas and mango. Spoon in alternate layers of yellow and pink into the glasses with the sauce. Sprinkle with flaked almonds, add lime slices and strawberries around rim of glasses and serve immediately.

***Tofu Cheesecake
(Low sugar)

Base
6oz medium oatmeal
2oz sesame seeds, ground
water mix

Filling
3 10oz blocks firm silken tofu   *grated rind 2 lemons*
4 tablespoons maple syrup or more to taste
1/2 pint/280ml soya milk   *2 teaspoons natural vanilla essence*
4 heaped teaspoons agar agar flakes
1/4 pint/140ml apple juice   *1 jar sugar-free red fruit jam*

Method
Base

Mix oatmeal and sesame seeds and enough water to bind. Press out into loose bottom cake tin. Bake 20-25 mins 350°F/180°C Mark 5. Cool.

Filling

1. Put apple juice in a pan and sprinkle over agar flakes; slowly bring to boil, stir and simmer for 1 minute. Allow to cool slightly.

2. Liquidize together all the remaining ingredients except the jam. Add the agar mixture.

3. Pour over baked case and allow to set in the fridge. Spread jam over the top. Chill for at least 1 hour before removing from the tin.

Swedish Glace, *a creamy frozen dessert (above), is ideal for vegans, vegetarians and those that wish to avoid dairy products.*

Katherine Monbiot *creates some exciting items (left) in her video on vegan cooking which is available through our reader service.*

Aqua Libra *have combined with the Head Chef at Champneys to produce excellent meals (right). See page 78 for details.*

RECIPES BY SUE KREITZMAN

Soup and Pasta non-fat vegan, Cous Cous non-fat vegetarian

Creamy parsnip soup

A non-fat vegan recipe   Yields 2 1/4 pints (1.3 litres)

1 lge Spanish onion   *1 teasp. minced fresh ginger*
2 cloves garlic, crushed   *3 pts. (1700ml) stock*
1 teasp. garam masala   *1/4 teasp. cayenne pepper*
1lb (450gms) parsnips, peeled and diced
1 medium all-purpose potato, scrubbed and coarsely diced
Salt and freshly ground black pepper to taste

1.Combine onion, ginger, garlic and 1/2 pt. (300ml) stock in a heavy-bottomed soup pot. Cover and bring to a boil. Boil for 5-7 mins. Uncover, reduce heat and simmer, stirring until the onions are tender and amber brown and the liquid is about gone. Add in a splash of stock and stir and cook - scraping up the browned bits - for another minute or two more. Add the garam masala and cayenne and stir so that the onions are well coated with the spices.

2. Stir in the parsnips, potato and remaining stock. Simmer for 10 - 15 mins. until the parsnips and potatoes are very tender. Season with salt and pepper. Cool slightly.

3. Purée in batches in the liquidizer until smooth and velvety. (This soup should not be chunky.) Return to the pot. Heat gently, correct season-ing and serve.

From 'Slim Cuisine Diet' by Sue Kreitzman

MAIN COURSE

Pasta Primavera

A non-fat vegan recipe. Yields 1 1/2 pints (900ml)

6 oz (175gms) button mushrooms, quartered
1 bunch spring onions, trimmed and sliced thin
4 - 5 leaves of basil, shredded
1 red, 1 yellow pepper cut into their natural sections, peeled, and then cut into 1 inch squares
1 head fennel, trimmed, cut in half lengthways, and sliced
1 medium courgette trimmed and sliced about 1/2 inch (1cm) thick
4 fresh ripe tomatoes, cored, skinned, seeded and coarsely diced
Approx. 1/2lb (225gms) pasta (penne)
1 clove garlic, minced   8 fl. oz. (225ml) stock
Salt & freshly ground pepper   3-4 tblsps. grated Parmesan cheese

Method

1. In a big pot, heat up the water for the pasta.

2. Combine mushrooms, spring onions, garlic and about 5 fluid ounces (150ml) of stock in a flameproof casserole. Simmer until the vegetables are tender, and most of the liquid has cooked away.

3. Meanwhile, peel the peppers, and trim and slice the fennel and courgettes.

4. Add the peppers to the mushroom mix along with another few ounces of stock. Cook, stirring occasionally, until the peppers are almost tender. Add the fennel and courgettes - cook and stir a few minutes more, until all the vegetables are tender.

5. Meanwhile, put the tomatoes in a sieve and dip them into the boiling pasta water for ten seconds. Refresh briefly under cold water. Core, skin and seed the tomatoes, and then dice them roughly. Add to the vegetables along with the shredded basil. Season with salt and pepper. Let the mixture cook, gently, while the pasta cooks.

6. The sauce is ready when the tomatoes have lost their shape and the mixture is thick and savoury. When the pasta is al dente, drain it and toss it with the sauce directly in the casserole.

From 'Slim Cuisine, Italian Style' by Sue Kreitzman.

Ricotta and Mushroom Parcels

300ml (¹/₂pt) pancake batter
1 bunch of watercress, washed
    and drained
350g (12oz) closed cup
    mushrooms, wiped and very
    finely chopped
225g (8 oz) ricotta cheese
grated rind of 1 lemon
Salt and pepper
approx 40g (1¹/₂oz) margarine

Tomato Sauce
15ml (1 tablespoon) oil
1 onion, very finely chopped
125g (4oz) closed cup
    mushrooms, wiped and very
    finely chopped
190ml (¹/₃pt) water
225g (8oz) fresh tomatoes,
    peeled and finely chopped
3 bay leaves
30ml (2 tablespoons) tomato
    purée
salt and pepper
10ml (2 teaspoons) cornflour
10ml (2 teaspoons) water
To garnish: *lemon slices, sprig*
    of watercress

Use pancake batter to make 12 thin pancakes. Finely chop the watercress, then place in a basin with mushrooms, ricotta, lemon rind and seasoning and mix well. Divide mixture between the pancakes and make neat parcels. Place parcels, seam side down, into a greased dish. Dot each with a little more margarine then cover with aluminium foil. Bake in oven 180°C (350°F), Gas Mark 4, for 25 minutes.

To make tomato sauce, heat oil and cook onion and mushrooms until soft. Stir in water, tomatoes, bay leaves, tomato purée and seasoning. Bring to the boil and simmer for 10 minutes. Blend cornflour with water then stir into sauce. Bring to the boil, stirring. Discard bay leaves then pour sauce over parcels. Garnish with lemon slices and watercress.

Serves 4

This recipe is from the Mushroom Growers Association who have produced some excellent booklets on special diet meals. Send a SAE for details. *They have also produced 'The Mushroom Cookbook' a gflossy hardback at £7.50 inc. packing and postage.

*See 'Useful Contacts' for address.

Cous Cous with vegetables

A non-fat vegetarian recipe – yields 2 pts. (1.1 ltrs.) cous cous/3 pts (1.7ltrs.) vegetables

Vegetable curry ingredients
1 red, 1 green, 1 yellow pepper, peeled and coarsely chopped
1 head fennel, trim off tough outer layer and slice in $1/2$ in (-1cm) pieces
1 lb (450gms) courgettes, sliced into $1/2$ in (1cm) pieces

1 15oz tin (425gms) chick peas, drained	6 tblsps fresh lemon juice
4 fl. oz. (110ml) chopped, fresh parsley	4 cloves garlic, minced
2 fl. oz. (50ml) chopped fresh coriander	1 teasp. ground tumeric
3 carrots peeled & coarsely chopped	$1/4$ teasp. allspice
3 sm. turnips, peeled & coarsely chopped	$1/2$ teasp. ground ginger
$1 1/2$ teasp. ground coriander	$1/4$ teasp. ground cayenne pepper
1 teasp. paprika or paprika paste	$1 1/2$ teasp. ground cumin
1 lge. Spanish onion, coarsely chopped	24 fl. oz (670ml) stock
3 celery stalks, sliced into $1/2$ inch (1cm) pieces	

Cous cous ingredients

$3/4$ lb (350gms) cous cous	16 fl. oz. (425ml) boiling stock

Method

1. Spread onion pieces out in a frying pan. Cook over moderate heat until the onions are sizzling and sticking to the pan. Stir in 10 fluid ounces (300ml) of stock and let it bubble up, stirring up the brown deposits in the pan as it bubbles. Stir in celery, carrots, garlic, turnips, peppers, fennel and all spices. Turn the heat down and simmer, stirring frequently until the mixture is thick (not at all soupy) and the vegetables and spices are "frying" in their own juices.

2. Stir in the remaining vegetable curry ingredients, including the remaining stock. Season to taste with salt and freshly ground black pepper. Simmer gently, covered, for 15 minutes.

3. Combine cous cous with 16 fluid ounces (425ml) boiling stock in a large bowl. Let steep for 10 - 15 minutes, until the liquid is absorbed and the grains are tender. Fluff with a fork.

4. Serve the cous cous in a mound on a large plate surrounded by the vegetables, or vice versa.

From 'The Complete Slim Cuisine' by Sue Kreitzman

RECIPES BY BARBARA COUSINS

All wheat, sugar, salt, dairy and yeast free. Low fat or fat-free.

BREAKFAST

Pear and carob delight

Ingredients

8 level tblsps rice flour	*1/2 pt soya milk*
4 heaped tsps carob flour	*4 dsps coconut*
1 1/2 pts boiling water	
4 small or 2 large pears, peeled & cored	

Method

1. Mix the rice flour and the carob flour to a smooth paste with a little soya milk in a pan. Gradually add the remaining milk.

2. Cut the pears into very small, thin slices and add to the pan.

3. Add the boiling water and the coconut and bring the mixture to the boil stirring constantly.

4. Lower the heat and simmer for 5 - 10 minutes or until the pears are beginning to disintegrate, sweetening the mixture.

Serve hot or cold, as a breakfast cereal, snack or even pudding.

Banana and maize breakfast cereal

Ingredients

I vanilla pod, approx. 2" long	*8 level tblsps maize meal*
4 bananas, very finely sliced	*1/2 pt. soya milk*
1 1/2 pts. boiling water	*4 dsp raisins*

Method

1. If possible, soak the vanilla pod overnight in 1/4 pt. of boiling water.

2. Mix the maize meal to a smooth paste with the soya milk in a pan.

3. Add the vanilla pod, the boiled water, the bananas and the raisins.

4. Bring the mixture to the boil, stirring constantly.

5. Lower the heat and simmer for 5 - 10 mins. or until the banana is beginning to disintegrate.

6. Remove the vanilla pod and serve.

STARTER

Spinach and carrot timbale

Ingredients

1 lb spinach	1 egg
black pepper	1 clove garlic, crushed
1 lb carrots	toasted sesame seeds, sliced tomato.

Method

1. Cook the spinach (in the water which remains on the leaves after washing) for no more that 5 mins. Drain.

2. Cut the carrots into even sized pieces and cook until just tender.

3. Liquidize the spinach with the egg, the crushed clove of garlic and lots of black pepper, until a smooth purée is formed. (1 tblsp mayonnaise can be added if available.)

4. Purée the carrots with a little of the cooking liquid until smooth and soft; season with black pepper, (for extra flavour the carrots can be cooked in the juice of one orange).

5. Place a layer of carrot purée, then a layer of spinach purée into 4 - 6 ramekins or similar dishes.

6) Microwave for 50 seconds each or cook in the oven covered with foil for approx. 15 minutes or until the spinach purée is set. Reg. 6 - 400F - 200C.

7. Garnish half the surface with toasted sesame seeds and the other half with sliced tomatoes

MAIN COURSE

Nutty vegetable loaf

Ingredients

I onion, finely chopped	1 dsp olive oil
1/2 red pepper, finely diced	1 medium carrot, grated
1 medium baking apple, grated	4 oz cooked brown rice
2 oz finely ground nuts – almonds, hazelnuts, etc.	
1 dsp tomato purée	1/4 tsp mace
1/4 tsp cayenne pepper	black pepper
1/4 tsp thyme	1/4 tsp rosemary
1/2 level tsp mustard (optional)	

Continued overleaf

Nutty vegetable loaf – continued

Method

1. Sauté the onion and pepper in the oil until they soften and begin to brown. Add the grated carrot and apple and sauté for another 2 mins.

2. Add the remaining ingredients and mix well.

3. Place the mixture into a greased loaf tin and bake for approx. 40 mins. in the centre of the oven at Reg. 6, 400F, 200C.

Serve the loaf either hot or cold with vegetables or salad.

Broccoli and sweetcorn quiche

Ingredients

6-8 lge cabbage leaves
2 lge onions, chopped
3 eggs
black pepper
1 lb broccoli, broken into small florets
1 tblsp fresh parsley (1 tsp dried)

8 oz sweetcorn kernels
1 dsp olive oil
$3/4$ pt. soya milk
2 oz ground nuts

Method

1. Cook the cabbage leaves and the broccoli in boiling water for approx. 5 mins. until the cabbage leaves are soft enough to line the dish and the broccoli is still crunchy. Cool the broccoli quickly by dipping in cold water, to prevent over cooking.

2. Sauté the onions in the oil until beginning to brown and soften. Mix in the parsley.

3. Beat the eggs with the milk and season with black pepper.

4. Use the cabbage leaves to double line a deep 10" quiche dish.

5. Scatter half the onions over the base, then arrange the broccoli florets around the dish. Make sure the broccoli florets do not come above the top of the dish or they will brown and burn.

6. Fill the gaps between the broccoli with the sweetcorn, then scatter the remaining onions over the top. The dish should be well packed with vegetables.

7. Pour over the egg and milk mixture.

8. Scatter the ground nuts over the surface.

9. Bake in the centre of the oven Reg. 6, 400°F, 200°C for approx. 50-60 mins until the centre of the quiche is just setting.

SAUCE

Chick Pea Sauce

Ingredients

4 oz cooked chick peas

1 tblsp olive oil

1 tblsp tahini (optional)

stock in which chick peas are cooked

1 lge onion, diced

1 clove garlic, crushed

Method

1) Fry the onion and garlic in the oil until soft.

2) Purée the chick peas and the onion, add the garlic and tahini if being used.

3) Add sufficient chick pea stock to obtain the desired consistency. Use as a dip for vegetables, as a sauce with rice or vegetarian roasts, and with meat or fish dishes.

DESSERT

Apricot Mousse

Ingredients

3/4 pt. water   juice of 1/2 lemon

8 oz dried apricots (or a mixture of pears, apricots and peaches)

½ oz or 1 sachet of gelatine (or equivalent in agar-agar)

2 eggs, separated

Method

1. Soak the apricots overnight in the water. The apricots should be soft, if not bring to the boil, simmer for five minutes then allow to cool.

2. Purée the apricots and sufficient of the soaking liquid to make a soft purée.

3. Dissolve the gelatine in 2 tblsps of water in a bowl over a pan of hot water.

4. Add the gelatine, or agar-agar, and two egg yolks to the purée and mix well.

5. Leave the purée to cool until half set.

6. Whisk the egg whites in a bowl until stiff and fold into the half set purée mixture.

7. Place in a jelly mould or serving dish and leave in the fridge until set.

8. Decorate with nuts and fresh fruit

Cashew – Tamari Loaf

Shirl's scrumptious bake. One of the author's favourite savouries. Vegan, vegetarian and gluten-free

6 oz. cooked brown rice	*2 large chopped onions*
1 large crushed garlic clove or to taste	*6 oz. ground cashews*
2 oz. pine nuts	*6 oz. sliced courgettes*
2 medium grated carrots	*3/4 teasp. thyme*
1/2 teasp. rosemary	*2-3 tbsps. tamari soy sauce*

Method

Sauté onions and garlic in 1-2 tablespoons extra virgin olive oil till transparent. Add courgettes, pine nuts and herbs. Cook till courgettes are soft, then add tamari. Remove from heat and mix in other ingredients.

A layer of mushrooms in the centre of this loaf makes a tasty addition. 6 oz. sliced mushrooms sautéed in a little olive oil.

Press well down into a greased 2lb loaf tin. If incorporating a mushroom layer, put in half the mixture, then the cooked mushrooms, and finally put remainder of mixture over mushrooms. Cook for 50-60 minutes on Gas Mark 6. 200°C. Let stand in tin for 5 minutes before turning out.

MONTHLY SELECTION OF ORIGINAL MENUS

Aqua Libra have produced an attractive booklet under the title 'The Recipe Year' which gives a monthly selection of original menus created by Adam Palmer, Head Chef at Champneys.

The illustration on page 69 for August includes:–
Starter: Aqua Libra Melon and Lime Soup
Main Course: Celeriac and Wild Mushroom Terrine
Dessert: Poached Peach with Cinnamon Ice Cream

For a copy of their booklet which contains these recipes contact Callitheke UK Ltd. as listed in our Buyer's Guide.

Buyer's Guide

Alphabetical selection of firms supplying diet and health foods. See separate listing for product categories.

NOTE: Readers are advised that this is mainly a selection of products from manufacturers, or sole distributors. These products are generally available and suitable for the diets coded below. Most of the manufacturers' products are available from retailers, or cash and carry stores, and readers should in most cases start at that point for any enquiries. However, should you experience difficulty in obtaining what you want, ask for help from your local health food shop or, failing that, ask the manufacturer for information on your nearest supplier.

In addition to the coding below we have incorporated a product category section, but do bear in mind that products and manufacturers are constantly changing. The absence of any firm does not mean that they or their products are not suitable. Equally, the publishers cannot accept responsibility for the accuracy of any information listed which is mainly sent in or extracted from manufacturers' leaflets at the time of going to press.

Coding in this selection is as follows:–
A. Vegetarian
B. Vegan
C. Gluten-free
D. Slimming products
E. Dairy-free
F. Other dietary products
G. Health and diet drinks

ALPHABETICAL SELECTION

Applefords, (Margetts Foods Ltd.)
Clee Hill Road, Tenbury Wells, Worcs. WR15 8HD.
Tel: (0584) 810366   Fax: (0584) 861031/811914
A,C,D,F,G.

Aspall Cyder House Products
Aspall Hall, Debenham, Stowmarket, Suffolk. IP14 6PD.
Tel. (0728) 860510   Fax. (0728) 861031
A, B, G.

Bailey Milk Products Ltd
Denne House, Denne Road, Horsham,
W. Sussex RH12 1JS.
Tel. (0403) 273273   Fax. (0403) 273278.
A, C, D, F.

Batchelor Nutritional Advice Centre
FREEPOST, Dartford, Kent DA1 1UF
Tel.(0345) 581215
A, D, F.   SEE PROFILE

B. E. International Foods Ltd
Grafton House, Stockingswater Lane, Enfield, Middlesex, EN3 7JZ
Tel: (081) 804 8788   Fax: (081) 804 1006
G

Berrydales
Berrydale House, 5 Lawn Road, London NW3 OPS
Tel: (071) 722 2866 Fax: (071) 722 7685
A, B, C, E   SEE PROFILE

Blackfriars Bakery
Blackfriars Street, Leicester LE3 5DJ
Tel: (0533) 622836
A, B

--- PROFILE ---

FEW DRINKS in recent years have made such an impact as Aqua Libra, the sparkling, natural, herbal fruit juice drink. Aqua Libra is not just a flavoured water. It is a drink based on an original Swiss recipe which combines the best all-natural, alkaline-forming ingredients. These include pure fruit juices, vegetable aromatic extracts, aqueous infusions of sunflower and sesame seeds, fresh tarragon and Siberian ginseng. The result is a highly palatable drink, which is not only pleasant and refreshing but which also provides the means of maintaining the body's natural alkaline balance gently and naturally.

In today's fast moving environment it is not always easy to plan our diets and maintain a balanced lifestyle.

Keeping healthy is a balancing act between stress and relaxation, convenience foods and revitalising foods, and between acidity and alkalinity. Aqua Libra is available in 75cl bottles and individual 20cl bottles and a 25cl slimline can and has only 28 calories per 100ml.

Aqua Libra Dry, the stylish new taste sensation, is as natural and refreshing as Aqua Libra Original but distinctively drier. This new blend includes elder flower, angelica root and coriander seeds and is a perfect accompaniment to fine food.

Boots Health & Nutrition Centre
The Boots Co. PLC, Nottingham, NG2 3AA.
Tel. (0602) 495659
A, B, C, D, E, F, G.

The Bottle Green Drinks Company
Spring Mill Estate, Avening Road, Nailsworth, Glos GL6 0BS
Tel: (045383) 5794
G

Brewhurst Health Food Supplies
Abbot Close, Oyster Lane, Byfleet, Surrey KT147JP
Tel: (0932) 354211   Fax: (0932) 336235
A, B, C, D, E, F, G

Britannia Health Products Ltd
Forum House, Brighton Road, Redhill, Surrey RH1 6YS
Tel: (0737) 773741   Fax: (0737) 773116
A, B, D, F

Britimco Waterless Cookware (UK)
Brendon House, Langham Road,
Robertsbridge, East Sussex. TN32 5DT.
Tel. (0580) 880262.

SUPPLEMENTARY STATEMENT
Britimco supply 18/10 st.steel cookware with special thermic base for cooking without water - fat - salt, preserving nutrients for healthier eating, energy saving and special diets

British American Product Co Ltd
400 Cleveland Street, Birkenhead, Merseyside
Tel: (051) 6521576   Fax: (051) 6510208
A, B.

PROFILE

BATCHELORS name is well known for good, wholesome and colourful foods. Their products, which are extremely versatile, range from soups - Slim a Soups, Cup a Soups, Snack a Soups and Packet Soups. Savouries - with Pasta'n'Sauce, SuperNoodles, Savoury and Special Rices, and the new Delicately Flavoured range of Rices, Coriander and Herbs, Garlic and Butter, Provencale and Pilau. Beans and Bean Salads. Vegetables - both canned and dried.

Batchelors have launched the Batchelors Nutritional Advice Centre to provide helpful and impartial healthy eating advice. A selection of free leaflets are available on Sensible Slimming, Stress and Your Diet, Healthy Eating for Vegetarians, Healthy Eating for Young Children, Teenagers and in Retirement. Special notes also cover more specialised topics such as Diabetes and Gluten-Free diets.

To receive your free healthy eating leaflets, please call the Batchelors Nutritional Advice Centre on 0345 581215 (all calls in the UK are charged at local rate).

Brooke Bond Foods Ltd
Leon House, High Street, Croydon, Surrey, CR9 1JQ.
Tel. (081) 760-9257.   Fax. (081) 760 9340
A, B, G.

Callitheke (UK) Ltd, (Aqua Libra, Norfolk Punch & Purdey),
Templefields House, River Way, Harlow, Essex. CM20 2EA.
Tel. (0279) 639 852   Fax. (0279) 635 530
A, B, G.   SEE PROFILE

Cauldron Foods Ltd
149 South Liberty Lane, Ashton Vale Trading Estate,
Bedminster, Bristol BS3 2TL
Tel: (0272) 632835   Fax: (0272) 231427
A, B, C.

Caws Cenarth Welsh Cheese
Fferm Glyneithinog Pontsell, Boncath, Dyfed.
SA37 0LH.
Tel. (0239) 710432
A

Cawston Vale
The Winery, Cawston, Norwich, NR10 4BQ.
Tel. (0603) 871444   Fax. (0603) 872718
G.

PROFILE

BERRYDALES, started in 1990 by Michelle Berriedale-Johnson, a free-lance food writer whose family had developed dairy product allergies, sell a range of five dairy-free 'ice creams' - Honey Vanilla, Maple and Walnut, Ginger and Honey, Chocolate and Berry. The ices are made from organic tofu and soya milk and are therefore not only dairy-free but low in fat and vegetarian. These come in 100 ml, 500 ml and 2 litre sizes.

Part of the Berrydales' success is due to their publishing ventures.They produce a quarterly 'Special Diet News' packed with information for readers interested in special diets and healthy eating, and, in September, published 'Berrydales Special Diet Cookbook' containing 50 recipes (all of which are dairy, gluten, egg or sugar free) and lots of product information.

They have also just launched a range of six microwavable vegetarian frozen ready meals: Vegetable couscous, Spiced chick peas with ginger, Wild rice risotto with pine nuts (all dairy, gluten and egg free); Leek and mushroom bake and Mediterranean Bean ratatouille (gluten and egg free) and Pasta Primavera.

Berrydales' products are available from health food stores and selected supermarkets. See Buyer's Guide for address and telephone number.

Cereal Partners UK (Shredded Wheat)
1 Bridge Road East, Welwyn Garden City, Herts. AL7 1RR
Tel. (0707) 325100   Fax: (0707) 334669
A

Chalice Foods Ltd
Leroy House, 436 Essex Road, London N1 3QP.
Tel. (071) 226 5481   Fax. (071) 226 9658
A, B, F.

Copella Fruit Juices
Hill Farm, Boxford, Colchester, CO6 5NY   Tel.
(0787) 211 396   Fax. (0787) 210 496
Code G.

C. P. C. (UK) Ltd
Caterplan Division, Claygate House, Littleworth Road, Esher, Surrey, KT10 9PN.
Tel. (0372) 462181   Fax. (0372) 468775
A, G.

Dalepak Foods PLC
Dale House, Leeming Bar, Northallerton, N. Yorks. DL7 9DQ.
Tel. (0677) 424111   Fax. (0677) 424443
A

Dietade Foods (Margetts Foods Ltd)
Clee Hill Road, Tenbury Wells, Worcs WR15 8HD
Tel. (0584) 810 366   Fax. (0584) 810 617
A, B, C, D, F, & G.

The Dietburger Co. Ltd
Shirley Avenue, Stoneygate, Leicester LE2 3NB.
Tel. (0533) 702211   (081) 758 9008   (081) 788 3629
A, B, E.   SEE HALDANE PROFILE

Docker Foods Ltd
Unit 3, Westfield Road, Southam, Warwicks CV33 0JH
Tel: (0926) 814242   Fax: (0926) 817319
A

PROFILE

THE BOOTS HEALTH & NUTRITION CENTRE offers an advice and information service on all aspects of diet and health.

Boots stock a wide variety of slimming and healthy food products, vitamins, minerals and dietary supplements, diabetic foods and diet drinks.

They also have a range of products which are suitable for vegetarian/vegans, gluten-free diets, lactose-free diets, egg-free and maize-free diets.

Specific nutritional services include computer diet analysis and the Shapers slimming pack.

See the Buyer's Guide listing for telephone and address.

Doves Farm Foods Ltd
Salisbury Road, Hungerford, Berks. RG17 0RF.
Tel. (0488) 684880 Fax. (0488) 685235
A, B, C, F.   SEE PROFILE

Eisberg, Hedges & Butler
Bass Brewers South
Rivergate House, Newbury Business Park, London Road, Newbury, Berks RG13
Tel: (0635) 552222   Fax: (0635) 46027
G

Elixir Deluxe Ltd
Zytek House, London Road, Bassetts Pole, Sutton Coldfield B75 55A
Tel: (021) 323 2228   Fax: (021) 323 2210
G

Everfresh Natural Foods
Gatehouse Close, Aylesbury, Bucks HP19 3DE
Tel: (0296)25333   Fax (0296) 22545
A B C E

Evian (Agencies) Ltd
4 Hillgate Place, 18-20 Balham Hill, London SW12 9ER
Tel. (081) 673 8717   Fax. (081) 673 7211
G

Foodwatch International (Green Farm Nutrition Centre)
Burwash Common, East Sussex. TN19 7LX
Tel. (0435) 882 482   Fax. (0435) 882 929
A, B, C, D, & F.   SEE PROFILE

─────────── PROFILE ───────────

DOVES FARM FOODS LTD. was started by Michael and Clare Marriage in 1978 and they haven't had a chance to look back since.

Their highly flexible milling system offers a vast selection of organic and speciality flours in both industrial size sacks and retail packets. Their 1 kg flour packets can be seen on most supermarket shelves and with their unique and highly colourful designs they instantly become the centre of attention.

As well as flours, they market a dynamic and exciting range of organic breakfast cereals and biscuits. Doves Farm are a leading light in the world of organic foods, continually breaking new ground with innovative products and packaging, for instance their latest range of 100% organic breakfast cereals in recycled packets.

Doves Farm Foods are a highly ethical food manufacturer whose emphasis on due diligence and stringent quality assurance has brought them unprecedented years of growth in times when others have flinched in the face of economic recession. With a committed team of knowledgeable specialists they are an ideal ally for any food manufacturer wishing to source organic and specialist flours.

All their organic products are certified by the Soil Association. For address, etc. see Buyer's Guide.

Foundation Foods Co
Chantry Place, Headstone Lane, Harrow, Middx. HA3 6NY.
Tel. (081) 420 1210   Fax. (081) 420 1691
Distributors of frozen vegetarian and speciality foods

General Designs Ltd
P. O. Box 38E, Worcester Park, Surrey, KT4 7LX.
Tel. (081) 337 9366   Fax. (081) 330 6248
A, B, C, F.

Goodlife Foods
53 Lancaster Road, London. N4 4PL.
Tel: (0925) 837810 Fax: (0925) 838648
A.   SEE PROFILE

Goodness Foods
South March, Daventry, Northants. NN11 4PH.
Tel. (0327) 706611   Fax. (0327) 300436
Natural Foods Wholesaler. Information on special diet products
Over 4000 different product lines

granoVita UK Ltd
Ambron House, Eastfield Road, Wellingborough, Northants NN8 1QX
Tel (0933) 272440   Fax (0933) 273729
A, B, C, D, E, G.   SEE PROFILE

PROFILE

FOODWATCH, the well known allergy food specialists, have sold their mail order business to Green Farm. Established in 1979, Green Farm is renowned for its comprehensive range of natural health products and nutritional advice. The company specialises in supplying allergy free foods and the highest quality vitamins, minerals and special supplements plus the Natren range of probiotics.

Green Farm Foodwatch products include foods suitable for those requiring specialised diets for M.E., Candida, Diabetes, Allergies, etc. This range includes gluten free, grain free, wheat free, dairy free, sugar free, egg free, soya free, low sodium, low fat, organic, vegetarian and vegan foods.

Nutritionists are available to advise practitioners and members of the general public on choosing the healthiest and most appropriate diet, and can give information on the use of vitamins, minerals and other supplements available by mail order from their Green Farm Catalogue and also through selected health food stores and chemists, under their own Natural Flow label and under the Nature's Plus or Natren name. Foodwatch products are currently only available via mail order. See Buyer's Guide for address and telephone number.

Green Dragon Animal Free Foods
15 Columshill Street, Rothesay, Isle of Bute, PA20 0DN.
Tel. (0700) 505117
A, B, E.

Greenbank Drinks Co Ltd (AME)
Church Row, Stranton, Cleveland TS24 7QS
G

Greenline Healthcare
Bix Manor, Bix, Henley-on-Thames RG9 4RS
Tel: FREEFONE 0800 585095   Fax: (0491) 411363
A B C D E G

Grove Fruit Products Ltd
Milton Hill, Abingdon, Oxon OX14 4DP
Tel: (0235) 831571 Fax: (0235) 834675
A G

Haldane Foods Group
Howard Way, Newport Pagnell, MK16 9PT. Tel. (0908)
211311   Fax. (0908) 210514
A, B, C, D, E, F.   SEE PROFILE

Handmade Flapjack Co
Unit Y1, Herald Way, Binley Ind. Estate, Coventry CV3 2NY

Health & Diet Food Co. Ltd.
Europa House, Stoneclough Road, Redcliffe, Manchester
Tel. (0204) 707420   Fax. (0204) 792238
A, B, D, E, F.

PROFILE

GOODLIFE FOODS are specialist manufacturers of meat free convenience foods. The Company was set up in 1981 and has kept pace with the rising tide of demand for vegetarian products. The range consists of frozen, chilled and dried convenience foods suited to both vegetarians and to those cutting down on meat for health or ethical reasons.

The products are high quality alternatives to meat - not meat substitutes - and the range draws inspiration from both Eastern and Western styles of cooking.

Many of the ingredients used are unrefined fibre rich foods and many are organically grown to Soil Association Standards. No artificial ingredients or preservatives are used and the Goodlife factory is dedicated solely to meat-free production. The packaging is printed on recycled board.

Chilled and frozen products: Vegetable & Sesame Cutlets, Mexican Cutlets, Tandoori Cutlets, Nut Cutlets, Herb Bean Bangers, Spicy Bean Bangers, Falafel. Available from major supermarkets and Health Stores nationwide. Dried products: Vegetable Biriyani, Chow Mein, Pillau Rice, Cous Cous with lentils, Falafel, Vegetable Grills (Tandoori, Nut and Mexican flavours). Available from selected Health Stores. See Buyer's Guide for address and telephone number.

H. J. Heinz & Co. Ltd
Hayes Park, Hayes, Middx. UB4 8AL.
Tel. (081) 573 7757   Fax. (081) 848 2429
A, C, D.

Itona Products Ltd
Itona Works, Leyland Mill Lane, Wigan. WN1 2SB.
Tel. (0942) 34761/5
A, B, C, E, F, G.

JRJ Trading Company
PO Box 1298, London N20 0YT
Tel: (0707) 390 251   Fax: (0707) 390252
A, B

W. Jordan (Cereals) Ltd
Holme Mills, Biggleswade, Beds. SG18 9JX.
Tel. (0767) 318222.
A, F.

Kallo Foods Ltd
29 Groveley Road, Sunbury on Thames, Middx. TW16 7JZ.
Tel. (081) 890 8324   Fax. (081) 890 7307.
A, B, C, F, G.

--- **PROFILE** ---

granoVita UK started trading in Britain under its own name in late 1991. However, its parent company De-Vau-Ge granoVita has been supplying the British health food trade for many years under private labels. De-Vau-Ge granoVita has been producing natural products for over 95 years.

A wide range of products are available. Organic Soya milks include 'no sugar added' and 'sweetened with Apple extract' brands in addition to the Low Fat Soya milk which is free of Lactose. They also supply in Strawberry and Banana flavoured milk. Another 'special' is their Vitaslim meal range - a slimming aid formulated for the health food market, being 100% dairy free and sweetened with fruit sugar. These rich and creamy meal replacements come in 5 varieties: Banana, Chocolate, Peach, Strawberry, and Vanilla.

granoVita produces lactose free natural margarines in Sunflower and Vegetable varieties with added calcium.

Pates in tubes come in Vegetable, Herb Provence, Wild Mushroom and Paprika. Spreads in Chubb Packs come in Vegetable, Mushroom, Olive and Mixed Herbs and are also available in tins. Their Vegetable Wieners are vacuum packed for freshness and have organic tofu and other selected ingredients which give a smooth texture and a wonderful taste. The same excellence applies to their Vegetable Frankfurters. For that replacement savoury granoVita protein foods include Nut Luncheon, Vegetable Hotpot, Cashew Nut, Nut and Herb, Vegetable Loaf Mix and are versatile meals for any occasion.

Kellogg Co. of Great Britain Ltd
Kellogg Building, Talbot Road, Manchester, M16 0PU.
Tel. (061) 869 2000   Fax. (061) 869 2100.
A, B, D, F.

Kemps Frozen Yogurt, P A Ross (Food Brokers) Ltd
Ruskin Chambers, Drury Lane, Knutsford, Cheshire WA16 6HA
Tel: 0565 755500   Fax: 0565 654282
D, F.   SEE PROFILE

Kraft General Foods Ltd
St. George's House, Bayshill Road, Cheltenham, Glos. GL50 3AE.
Tel. (0242) 236101   Fax. (0242) 512084
A, B, C, E, F.

Leisure Drinks PLC
24 Willow Road, Trent Lane, Castle Donington, Derby. DE7 2NP.
Tel. (0332) 850616   Fax. (0332) 850605
A, B, G.

Life Stream Research UK
Ash House, Stedham, Midhurst, West Sussex. GU29
0PT. Tel. (073 081) 3642
A, B, C, D, F.

The London Herb & Spice Co Ltd (Premier Teas)
P O Box 2525, Birmingham B1 1PH
Tel: 021 459 1199
G

Manna Food Co Ltd
The Cart Barn, Burwash Road, Heathfield, E Sussex, TN21 8QY
Tel: (0435) 867249   Fax: (0435) 867250
A, B

PROFILE

THE HALDANE FOODS GROUP is Europe's largest health food manufacturing group which incorporates twelve companies within the UK - Dietburger Co, Direct Foods, Genice Foods, Granose Foods, Haldane Foods, Realeat Foods, Regular Tofu, Saucemasters, Snackmasters, Unisoy Milk'n By-Products, Vegetarian Cuisine and Vegetarian Feasts.

The Group's range of more than 250 ambient, chilled and frozen products covers all sectors of the vegetarian and health food markets. It includes vegeburgers, soups, condiments, rices, soya milk, complete vegetarian meals (frozen and unfrozen), dry vegetarian mixes, margarines, yogerts, non-dairy frozen desserts, spreads, vegetarian cheeses, snack bars, vegetarian snack meals in pots, tinned vegetarian protein foods and Quorn meals.

These healthy foods are available from all health food stores, many supermarkets and multiple grocers and chemists with a health food section.

Haldane has produced two recipe booklets containing suggestions for tasty vegetarian meals. One is based on Sosmix and Burgamix savoury premixes and the other on Realeat Vegeburgers and Vegebangers. They are available free of charge from Haldane Foods Group, Howard Way, Newport Pagnell, Bucks. MK16 9PY.

Marigold Health Foods
Unit 10, St Pancras Commercial Centre, 63 Pratt Street, London NW1 0BY
Tel: (071) 267 7368
A B C D E F G   SEE PROFILE

Martlet Natural Foods
Horam Manor, Horam, Heathfield,
East Sussex. TN21 0JA
Tel. (043 53) 2254 Fax. (043 53) 3218
A, B, D.

W T Maynard & Son & Co Ltd
Bindon Road, Taunton, Somerset TA2 6AB
Tel: (0823) 257922   Fax: (0823) 333328
A

Meridian Foods Ltd
Corwen, Clwyn. LL21 9RR
Tel. (0490) 413151   Fax. (0490) 412032
G.

Milford of London
4 Bond Street, London E15 1 LT
Tel: (081) 519 4762
G

Milram QUARK, Capital Foods Ltd
259 Sileby Road, Barrow-upon-Soar, LEICS LE12 8LP
Tel: (0509) 814770
A

Modern Health Products Ltd (G R Lane)
Sisson Road, Gloucester. GL1 3QB.
Tel. (0452) 524 012   Fax. (0452) 300 105
A, B, C, D, F.

——————— PROFILE ———————

KEMPS FROZEN YOGURT has been a phenomenal success in the USA, where it is the nation's best selling brand. In fact it presently out-sells rival Haagen Dazs 9-1. In just six months, since the initial launch date, Kemps has attained UK brand leader status.

Made from all natural ingredients with an active yogurt base, Kemps tastes just like full dairy ice cream, yet contains less than half the fat, fewer calories and virtually cholesterol-free.

Revolutionising the eating habits for consumers, Kemps offers all of the taste of premium ice cream which is available in five mouth watering varieties:– FRENCH VANILLA – real natural vanilla with a creamy texture; CALIFORNIA STRAWBERRY – with real pieces of strawberry; CARAMEL NUTTY FUDGE – with the Mars Snicker bar swirled in; TOASTED ALMOND FUDGE – toasted almond slices nestled in a rich chocolate base; CHOCOLATE TOFFEE CRUNCH – French Vanilla base with pieces of crunchy toffee.

Seen as the healthy alternative for the health conscious consumer, Kemps is asking Britain to give in to Kemptations!

Mornflake Oats Ltd
North Western Mills, Crewe, Cheshire, CW2 6HP.
Tel. (0270) 213 261   Fax. (0270) 500 291
A B

The Nestlé Co. Ltd Healthcare Division
St. George's House, Croydon, Surrey. CR9 1NR.
Tel. (081) 686 3333   Fax. (081) 686 6072
A, C, D, F, G.

New Zealand Natural Food Co
9 Holt Close, Highgate Wood, London. W10 3HW.
Tel. (081) 444 5660
A, B, F.

Northumbrian Fine Foods PLC
Dukesway, Team Valley, Tyne & Wear. NE11 0QP
Tel. (091) 487 0070
A, B, C, F.

Nutricia Dietary Products Ltd
494/496 Honeypot Lane, Stanmore, Middx. HA7 1JH.
Tel. (081) 951 5155   Fax. (081) 951 5623
A, B, C, D, F.   SEE PROFILE

Onken
P. O. Box 700, London SW14 7NP.
Tel. (081) 876 4520   Fax. (081) 876 0221
A, C, D

PROFILE

MARIGOLD HEALTH FOODS was established in 1977 and is now a leading supplier of products for health and special diets.

Their famous Swiss Vegetable Bouillon is available in original and reduced salt versions. It is very versatile, being delicious as an instant stock, seasoning or hot drink. The original recipe is gluten-free and yeast free while the reduced salt version is dairy free and yeast free.

Another unique and popular product is Marigold Braised Tofu. Made to a special recipe, this highly nutritious vegan delicacy is tasty in salads, sandwiches, grilled or stir-fried, hot or cold.

Marigold Engevita Nutritional Yeast Flakes are a vegan food with a cheesy nutty taste made from primary inactive yeast, cultured from molasses. An ideal condiment for soups, stews, salads and toppings, they are rich in B vitamins and minerals.

Other products in the range include the vegan mayonnaise style Marigold Soy Dip and pre-packed vegetarian cheddar and parmesan cheese.

Marigold is the importer of Golden Temple Yogi Teas which contain only spices and no caffeine - an ideal substitute for tea and coffee. See their Buyer's Guide listing.

Perrier (UK) Ltd
Trinity Court, Church Street, Rickmansworth, Herts. WD3 1LD.
Tel. (0923) 897700   Fax. (0923) 897 608
G.

Plamil Foods Ltd
Plamil House, Bowes Well Gardens, Folkestone, Kent. CT19 6PQ.
Tel. (0303) 850015   Fax: (0303) 850015
A, B, C, E, F.

Ploughshares
54 Roman Way, Glastonbury, Somerset, BA6 8AD Tel: 0458 35233/31182
A, B, C, E, F   *Residential Dip. Courses in Vegan Cuisine*

Quaker Oats Ltd
P O Box 24, Bridge Road, Southall, Middx. UB2 4AG.
Tel. (081) 574 2388   Fax. (081) 574 6615
A, B.

RHM Soft Drinks
Chapel House, Alma Road, Windsor Berks
Tel: (0753) 857123   Fax: (0753) 846537
G

The Ryvita Company Ltd
Parkstone, Dorset BH17 7NW
Tel: (0344) 487848
A, B, D

St. Giles Foods Ltd.
5 Church Estate, Slade Green Road, Slade Green, Kent, DA8 2JA.
A, B, C, E.

St. Ivel Ltd
Interface Business Park, Wootten Bassett, Swindon, Wilts. SN4 8QE.
Tel. (0793) 848444   Fax. (0793) 843146
A, F.

PROFILE

IN THE 13th CENTURY the monks at Welle Manor devised a recipe for a unique drink containing over thirty different herbs and spices. So carefully made was this drink, that the monks gathered certain herbs at specific phases of the moon and meticulously pounded them by hand with a pestle and mortar.

Today Norfolk Punch is still produced to the original recipe, including preparation of the punch in this old tradition. The infusion of herbs such as feverfew, fennel and camomile impart to the punch its unique, aromatic character and fruity depth of flavour. The herbs and spices are infused in the natural Norfolk water containing selenium, a rare trace element which is increasingly believed to play an important role in maintaining good health.

These days Norfolk Punch makes no curative or medical claims other than to relax, warm and cheer, but in days of yore the recipe was relied upon to provide the relief for most ills.

Available in Original and Apple variety, Norfolk Punch is best served piping hot or chilled over ice. It is completely healthy and natural, with no additives, preservatives or colourants.

R. M. Scott Ltd
30 Greyfriars Road, Ipswich, Suffolk IP1 1UP
Tel: (0473) 252714
A, B, C

Sojasun, Triballats
Springhead Road, Enterprise Park, North Gravesend, Kent DA11 8HN.
Tel: 0474 333331
A B C E

SUPPLEMENTARY STATEMENT
Sojasun and Soji are the only chilled desserts of their kind, Sojasun for adolescents and adults, Soji for children

Sorelle (Merrydown Wines PLC)
Horam Manor, Horam, Heathfield, E. Sussex TN21 0JA
Tel: 04353 2254   Fax: 04353 3218
G

Soya Health Foods Ltd
Unit 4, Guiness Road, Trafford Park, Manchester. M17 1AU.
Tel.(061) 872 0549   Fax: (061) 872 6776
A, B, E, F.

--- PROFILE ---

NUTRICIA DIETARY PRODUCTS LTD. are one of the largest companies catering for specialised diets. A large variety of foods are available for gluten-free and low protein diets and other food intolerances. These include bread, rolls, flour replacements, biscuits, cakes, pasta and egg replacers. Products are produced using the latest technology with great attention being given to quality.

The products may also be free of other ingredients such as wheat, gluten, milk, lactose, egg or soya. Many can be obtained on prescription for eligible medically diagnosed conditions such as coeliac disease. Nutricia products are available from health food stores and chemists throughout the U.K. and in Europe under the Glutafin, Rite Diet and Loprofin names.

Literature and helpful information can be obtained from Customer Services: • Product guides • Recipe booklets • A consumer magazine – Eat Well • Customer services help line • Mail order facility • Cookery demonstrations • A national network of approved stockists. The company has years of experience in this field and continues to be at the forefront of new research and development.

Nutricia's products help provide taste, satisfaction and variety for people with restricted diets. For further information call the Customer Services Department on 081 204 6968. See Buyer's Guide for address.

Dr Stuart's Botanical & Fruit Teas
308 High Street, Croydon, Surrey CRO 1NG
Tel: 081 686 8917   Fax: 081 681 0936
G

Suma Wholefoods
Dean Clough, Halifax. HX3 5AN.
Tel. (0422) 345513.
A, B

Swedish Glace, Winner (UK) Ltd
Davies House, Horn Lane, Acton, London W3 6QU
Tel: (081) 992 3444   Fax: (081) 992 0726
A E   SEE PROFILE

Thomas Symington & Co. Ltd
Sisson Road, Gloucester. GL1 3QB.
Tel. (0452) 524 012   Fax. (0452) 300 105
G

Thursday Cottage Ltd
Spaxton, Bridgwater, Somerset.
Tel. (0278) 67330

Total Yoghurt
Gordon Conrad Ltd., 182-196 Ilderton Road, London SE13 1TW
Tel: (071) 277 5171

R. Twining & Company Ltd
South Way, Andover, Hants SP10 5AQ
Tel (0264) 334477
G

—————————— PROFILE ——————————

THE VEGETARIAN SOCIETY is the main voice for vegetarians in Britain, who currently number almost four million. Established in 1847, the Society is dedicated to increasing the number of vegetarians in the UK to save animals, benefit human health, protect the environment and safeguard world food resources. A staff of 32, based at the Society's Altrincham headquarters, work towards this aim through active campaigning and education.

The growth of interest in vegetarianism in recent years has been mirrored by the expanding activities of the Society. These include the highly acclaimed Cordon Vert Cookery School, a merchandising department stocking the most comprehensive range of vegetarian cookbooks and literature available in the UK; a glossy, full-colour magazine, The Vegetarian, produced in-house and published 10 times a year; and the distinctive green seedling 'V' symbol, licensed for use only on those vegetarian products that meet the Society's exacting standards.

An in-house information and research unit sponsors scientific research in subjects related to vegetarianism and advises health professionals, the media and the public, as well as providing the background to all major campaigns. Telephone 061 928 0793 for more information.

Vandemoortele (UK) Ltd
Provamel, Ashley House, 86-94 High Street, HOUNSLOW, Middx. TU3 1HH.
Tel. (081) 570 4776   Fax: (081) 577 7441
A B E

Weetabix Ltd.
Burton Latimer, Kettering, Northants. NN15 5JR.
Tel (0536) 722181   Fax: (0536) 726148
A, B, D, F.

Weight Watchers from Heinz
Hayes Park, Hayes, Middx. UB4 8AL.
Tel. (081) 573 7757   Fax: (081) 848 2509
D.

Whole Earth Foods Ltd
269 Portobello Road, London. W11 lIR
Tel. (071) 229 7545   Fax: (071) 221 6416
A ,B, C, D, E, F, G

Winner Swedish Glace (UK) Ltd.
Davies House, Horn Lane, Acton, London W3 6QU
Tel: (081) 992 3444   Fax: (081) 992 0726
A, E   SEE PROFILE

PROFILE

THE SOCIETY FOR THE PROMOTION OF NUTRITIONAL THERAPY (SPNT) was founded in 1991 by Linda Lazarides, to promote greater understanding of the important role which nutrition can play in health care.

Nutritional therapy is a modern health care system. A number of different diets may be used - such as a hypoallergenic diet or a 'cleansing' diet. Practitioners also prescribe food supplements - vitamins, minerals, amino acids, essential fatty acids, etc. This is because it is quite common to have nutritional deficiency symptoms despite eating a good diet (usually when the digestion is faulty). Supplements are prescribed on an individual basis, and can provide extraordinary benefits when used under expert guidance.

Nutritional therapy is particularly effective for headaches or migraine, poor digestion, PMS, chronic fatigue, overweight, allergies, high cholesterol, irritable bowel syndrome, bloating, skin problems, mood swings, and high blood pressure.

Any person who is interested in nutrition can join the SPNT. Benefits of membership include a quarterly magazine on nutritional therapy, and access to seminars and workshops at reduced prices. Members can request a free list of practitioners in their area. To find out more, contact The Secretary, SPNT, 2 Hampden Lodge, Hailsham Road, Heathfield, East Sussex. TN21 8AE.

Product Categories

Readers can refer to the diet in which they are interested to find the names of suppliers in that category. Although this listing cannot be fully comprehensive we have, where possible, listed brand names.

CODING:

1. Biscuits, Cakes, Bread.
2. Breakfast Foods
3. Cheese Products
4. Desserts
5. Fats
6. Health Drinks
7. Savouries
8. Soups
9. Soya "Dairy" Products
10. Spreads & Dressings

VEGETARIAN

Applefords	1, 6, 10.
Bailey	3, 4. Sudmilch, Patros
Batchelor	SEE PROFILE
Berrydales	SEE PROFILE
Blackfriars Bakery	1
Britannia	1
Britimco	SEE SUPPLEMENTARY STATEMENT
British American Products Ltd.	5. Ashland
Boots	SEE PROFILE
Brooke Bond	6, 7, 8 OXO
Brewhurst	All categories
Cauldron Foods Ltd.	4, 7, 10
Chalice Foods Ltd.	10
Caws Cenarth	3
Cereal Partners	2 Shredded Wheat
C. P. C. Ltd.	7, 10 Marmite, Mazola, Knorr, Napolina
Dalepak Foods plc	7
Dietade	4, 6
The Dietburger Co. Ltd	7
Docker Foods Ltd	7 Peakhouse Pantry
Doves Farm Foods Ltd	SEE PROFILE
Everfresh	1, 4, 7. Sunnyvale
Foodwatch International	SEE PROFILE
Foundation	4, 7, 9
General Designs Ltd.	1, 7. Ener-G, Pastariso
Goodlife Foods	SEE PROFILE

Goodness Foods	All categories
granoVita	SEE PROFILE
Grove Products	4
Green Dragon Animal Free Foods	3, 10
Haldane Foods Group	SEE PROFILE
Handmade Flapjack Co	1
Health & Diet Food Co. Ltd.	1, 2, 6, 8.
H. J. Heinz & Co. Ltd.	1, 3, 4, 7, 8, 10.
Itona Products Ltd.	1, 4, 7. Granny Ann, Golden Archer
J R J Trading	3, 10. Redwood Vegetarian Rashers
W Jordan	2
Kallo Foods Ltd.	1, 2, 8
Kellogg Co. of Great Britain Ltd	2
Kemps Frozen Yogurt	SEE PROFILE
Kraft Foods Ltd	2, 3, 4, 6, 10
Leisure Drinks	6, 10 Country Man Veg.Pate
Life Stream	1, 6
Manna Food Co	1
Marigold	3, 6, 7, 8, 10
Maynard	7
Milram Quark	7
Modern Health	1, 6, 8, 10 Vecon, Natex, Vessen
Mornflake Oats Ltd	2
The Nestle Co. Ltd.	2, 10
New Zealand Natural Food Co	10
Norfolk Punch	Xmas Pudding See also PROFILE
Northumbrian Fine Foods plc	1, 2, 3, 7, 10 Prewetts, Sunwheel, Kalibu
Nutricia	SEE PROFILE
Onken	4
Plamil Foods Ltd.	3, 4, 6, 7, 9, 10
Ploughshares	1, 4, 7
Quaker Oats Ltd.	2
Ryvita	1, 2
St Ivel	
Sojasun	4, 9
Soya Health Foods Ltd.	4, 7, 9. Sunrise
Swedish Glace	SEE PROFILE
Suma	2, 4, 5, 7, 8, 10
Tilda Rice	
Vandemoortelle (Provamel)	4, 6, 9
Weetabix Ltd.	2
Weight Watchers from Heinz	1, 3, 4, 7, 8, 10.
Whole Earth Foods Ltd.	2, 6, 7, 10

VEGAN

Aspall	6, 10
Batchelor Foods	SEE PROFILE
Bailey	4
Berrydale	SEE PROFILE
Blackfriars Bakery	1
Boots	SEE PROFILE
Brewhurst	All categories
Britannia	1
British American	5 Ashland
Brooke Bond	7, 8, 10 OXO
Cauldron	4, 7, 10
Cereal Partners UK	2 Shredded Wheat, Shreddies
Chalice	10
Dietade	4
Dietburger	7
Doves	SEE PROFILE

Everfresh	1, 4, 7
Foodwatch	1, 2, 4, 5, 7, 8, 10
General Designs	1, 7 Ener-G, Pastariso rice pasta
Goodness Foods	All categories
granoVita	SEE PROFILE
Green Dragon	3, 10
Greenline	
Haldane	SEE PROFILE Granose
Handmade Flapjack	1
Health & Diet Food Co	1, 2 Holly Mill
Itona	1, 4, 7 Granny Ann, Golden Archer
J R J Trading	3, 7, 10 Redwood Rashers, SerenDIPity
W Jordan	2
Kallo	3, 6, 8 Just Bouillon
Kellogg's	2 Summer Orchard Muesli
Kraft	2, 10
Leisure	10 Country Man Veg.Pate
Lifestream	1
Manna	1
Marigold	3, 6, 7, 8, 10
Modern Health Products	6, 8, 10 Natex, Vessen
Mornflake Oats Ltd	2
New Zealand Natural Food Co	10
Northumbrian Fine Foods plc	1, 2, 4, 10 Sunwheel, Kalibu, Prewetts
Nutricia	SEE PROFILE
Plamil	3, 4, 6, 7, 9, 10
Quaker Oats Ltd	2 Oatbran Crispies, Puffed Wheat
Ryvita	1, 2 High Fibre Cornflakes
Sojasun	4, 9
Soya Health Foods Ltd	4, 7, 9, 10 Sunrise
Suma	2, 4, 5, 7, 8, 10
Tilda Rice	
Vandemoortelle	4, 9 Provamel
Weetabix	2
Weight Watchers from Heinz	1, 4, 7, 8, 10
Whole Earth	2, 6, 7, 10

GLUTEN-FREE

Applefords	1
Berrydales	SEE PROFILE
Bailey Milk Products Ltd	4 Country Love
Boots	SEE PROFILE
Brewhurst	All categories
Cauldron	7, 10
Dietade	4, 6
Doves Farm Foods Ltd.	1
Everfresh	1, 4, 7 Sunnyvale
Foodwatch International	1, 2, 10 Versaloaf SEE PROFILE
General Designs	1, 7 Ener-G, Pastariso
Goodness Foods	All categories
granoVita	SEE PROFILE
Haldane	SEE PROFILE
Itona Products Ltd.	1, 2, 4, 7, 9 GrannyAnn, Golden Archer
Kallo Foods Ltd	1, 2, 6, 8 Puffed rice, Just Bouillon
Kraft General Foods	3, 4, 5, 6, 10
Life Stream Research U.K.	1 Spirolight bars
Manna	1
Marigold	SEE PROFILE
Modern Health Products Ltd	6, 10 Thos Symington
Nestle	6 Slender, Build-Up
New Zealand Natural Food Co	10

Northumbrian Fine Foods plc	1, 2, 10 Sunwheel, Kalibu,
Nutricia SEE PROFILE	1, 2, 4, 7 Rite-Diet Juvela Glutafin GF
Onken	4
Plamil Foods Ltd	3, 4, 6, 7, 9, 10
Sojasun	4
Weight Watchers from Heinz	3, 4, 7, 8, 10
Whole Earth	6, 7, 10

SLIMMING PRODUCTS

Applefords	1, 6
Bailey Milk Products Ltd	4
Batchelor	SEE PROFILE
Boots	Shapers SEE PROFILE
Britannia	1 Slim'n'Fit, Leijfibre
Dietade	4, 6, 10
Foodwatch International	SEE PROFILE
granoVita	SEE PROFILE
Greenline	Lite Wate, Fibrina
Haldane	SEE PROFILE
Health & Diet Food Co Ltd	Slymbrand
Itona	7
Kellogg Co. of Great Britain Ltd	2
Kemps Frozen Yogurt	SEE PROFILE
Life Stream Research U.K.	1
Marigold	SEE PROFILE
Martlet	6
Modern Health Products Ltd	6, 10
Nestle	6
Nutricia	SEE PROFILE
Ryvita	1
Weetabix Ltd	2
Weight Watchers from Heinz	1, 3, 4, 7, 8, 10
Whole Earth Foods Ltd.	

DAIRY-FREE

Applefords	1
Berrydales	SEE PROFILE
Boots	SEE PROFILE
Brewhurst	All categories
The Dietburger Co Ltd	SEE HALDANE PROFILE
Everfresh	1, 4, 7
Foodwatch	SEE PROFILE
Goodness Foods	ALL
granoVita	SEE PROFILE
Green Dragon Animal Free Foods	3, 10
Haldane Foods Group	SEE PROFILE
Health & Diet Food Co Ltd	Slymbrand
Itona Products Ltd	1, 4, 7 Golden Archer
Kallo	Just Bouillon
Kraft Foods Ltd	10
Marigold	6 Swiss vegetable bouillon
New Zealand Natural Food Co Ltd	10
Nutricia	SEE PROFILE
Plamil Foods Ltd	3, 4, 6, 7, 10
Sojasun	4
Soya Health Foods Ltd	6, 9 Sunrise
Swedish Glace	SEE PROFILE
Vandemoortelle	4, 6, 9 Provamel
Weight Watchers from Heinz	1, 7, 8, 10
Whole Earth	2, 6, 7, 10

HEALTH & DIET DRINKS

Applefords — Organic Apple juice, fruit drinks
Aspall Cyder House Products — Organic Apple juice
Bottle Green Drinks Company — Citrus, elderflower cordials, presses
Boots — SEE PROFILE
Brewhurst
Brooke Bond Foods Ltd — Oxo, teas
Callitheke (UK) Ltd — SEE PROFILE
Cawston Vale — Pure fruit juices,
Copella Fruit Juices — Farm pressed English fruit juices
C. P. C. (UK) Ltd — Marmite, Bovril
Dietade — Diabetic/slimmers squashes
Eisberg — Low/no alcohol wines
Elixir — Herbal fruit multivitamin drinks
Evian — Mineral water, fruit juices
granoVita — Organic soya-milk drinks
Greenbank — AME - herbal vitaminised fruit juice
Greenline — Fibrina
Health & Diet Food — Pompadour herbal teas
Grove Products — Gingle - herbal apple based drink
Kallo Foods Ltd — Just Bouillon, Lima Yannoh coffee
Leisure Drinks plc — Volonte juices & nectars
Lifestream — Aloe Vera Juice
Martlet — Organic Apple Juice
Meridian — Meridian
Milford — Herbal teas
The Nestle Co. Ltd — Slender, Coffee, cocoa, fruit juices
Perrier (UK) Ltd — Spring water
RHM Soft Drinks — Just Juice, De L'ora, One Cal, Capri Sun
Sorelle — Peach based fruit drink
Thos Symington — Dandelion coffee, herbal teas
Twining & Co — Fine teas
Whole Earth — Gusto - apple juice based herbal drink

PROFILE

SWEDISH GLACE is new from Sweden but already it has established itself as one of the top quality NON-DAIRY ice creams in the UK.

Made by Winner, one of Sweden's leading ice cream and frozen dessert producers, SWEDISH GLACE contains no animal fats and is made from 100% organic whole soya beans. It is ideal for Vegetarians, Vegans and those allergic to dairy products, but the unashamed luxury of the chocolate and vanilla varieties deserves to be enjoyed by all lovers of ice cream!

Look out for the distinctive octagonal packs. SWEDISH GLACE has a competitive price at around £1.85 – £1.90 for the .75 litre pack.

Winner have been producing top quality ice-cream and frozen desserts for almost 30 years, so you can rest assured that Swedish Glace is no poor substitute. It offers a real alternative to premium dairy ice cream. Delicious on its own, as well as with sauces, fruit and in desserts, Swedish Glace makes a wonderful soya milkshake too.

For further information about SWEDISH GLACE see Buyers Guide.

Useful Contacts

AAA (Action Against Allergy) 24-26 High Street, Hampton Hill, Middlesex TW12 1PD   Fax. 081 943 3631

British Diabetic Association, 10 Queen Anne Street, London W1M 0BD Tel: 071 323 1531

British Diabetic Association, 7th Floor, Elizabeth House, 22 Suffolk Street, Queensway, Birmingham B1 1LS. Tel: 021 643 5483

British Health Food Trade Association & Health Food Manufacturers Association, Angel Court, High Street, Godalming, Surrey. GU7 1DT. Tel: 0483 426450

Coeliac Society of the UK, P. O. Box 220, High Wycombe, Bucks. HP11 2HY Tel: 0494 437278

Eating Disorders Association, Sackville Place, 44-48 Magdalen Street, Norwich, Norfolk NR3 1JE Tel: 0603 621414

The Jewish Vegetarian Society, 'Bet Teva', 853/855 Finchley Road, London, NW11 8LX. Tel: 081 455 0692

The Life Foundation, 15 Holyhead Road, Upper Bangor, Gwynedd, North Wales. LL57 2EG. Tel: 0248 370076

The Mushroom Growers' Association, 2 St. Pauls Street, Stamford, Lincs. PE9 2BE. Tel: 0780 66888 (3 lines)

National Association of Health Stores, Bastow House, Queens Road, Nottingham, NG2 3AS. Tel: 0602 866848.

Natural Health Network, Chardstock House, Chard, Somerset, TA20 2TL. Tel: 0460 63229.

Nutrition Association, 36 Wycombe Road, Marlow, Bucks. SL7 2HX

Society for the Promotion of Nutritional Therapy, 2 Hampden Lodge, Hailsham Road, Heathfield, East Sussex. TN21 8AE. Tel: 0435 867007.

The Soya Milk Information Bureau, P.O. Box 169, Banbury, Oxfordshire. OX16 9XE.

The Vegan Society, 7 Battle Road, St. Leonard's on Sea, East Sussex. TN37 7AA.

The Vegetarian Society (UK) Ltd., Parkdale, Dunham Road, Altrincham, Cheshire, WA14 4QG. Tel: 061 928 0793.

Women's Nutritional Advice Service, P. O. Box 268, Hove, East Sussex BN3 1RW Tel: 0273 771367

EXHIBITIONS TO VISIT

An exhibition that has captured the hearts and minds of anyone interested in food and drink has to be the BBC Good Food Cooking and Kitchen Show. Held annually at the N.E.C. Birmingham, it attracts thousands of enthusiasts. You can sample delicious new foods and wines, discover the newest kitchens and cookware, compare appliances, all under one roof.

Every year a new show mixes the essential ingredients of variety, for example items like Celebrity Theatre with exciting demonstrations by your favourite celebrity cooks; a Wine Fair brings together the country's best known experts, finest wine producers and top wine retailers; the GOURMET MARKET offers the most tantalising tastes from all over the world.

The HEALTHY EATING CENTRE shows that healthy meals, vegetarian food and dieting don't have to be boring; FRESH FOOD FOCUS brings the best of fresh produce, HOME BAKERY shows all you need to know about baking cakes and bread.

The catering demonstration area provides non-stop workshops and there are plenty of opportunities for tasting the end-products in the various catering facilities.

It is an ideal day out for visitors and an excellent exhibition to display and sell products.

The 1993 exhibition is open at the N.E. C. from 25th – 28th November.

Make a note in your diary now:
Organisers Consumer Exhibitions Ltd., 243/253 Lower Mortlake Road, Richmond, Surrey, TW9 2LS. Telephone: 081 948 1666.

──────────── EXHIBITIONS TO VISIT ────────────

Healthy Eating at
THE HEALTH SHOW
The UK's Greatest Health and Fitness Show

The Health Show incorporates a Healthy Eating section which attracts thousands of visitors.

Trade and public have been attending the Health Show for over 10 years and, in 1993, it moves into the National Hall at Olympia.

It's a grand day out for anyone interested in natural health and this is especially true for those keen to see and taste some of the many food products on display.

The 1993 exhibition opens on 10th June and closes on the 13th.

'Catering for Health and Special Diets' will be there - just inside the main entrance of the National Hall.

Enquiries:
071 370 8185

Organisers:
Philbeach Events Ltd.

A Worthy cause to support

Friedreich's Ataxia is a crippling disease of childhood. A progressive disabling disease of the nervous system. There is currently no cure for it. But, thanks to the Friedreich's Ataxia Group, which has funded over £1 million, during the past decade tracking down the gene responsible, there is hope. Simply to maintain the research at its present level will cost another £1 million, over the next three years. It is money that must be found because many sufferers just can't wait another ten years for the group to raise it! Please, will you help?

Send enquiries or donations to:
The Hon. Treasurer, Friedreich's Ataxia Group,
Copse Edge, Thursley Road, Elstead, Godalming,
Surrey. GU8 6DJ

READER SERVICE

On behalf of readers, the publishers would be pleased to obtain further information on any product or service mentioned in this book. Please write to the address below stating clearly the information required and send with a large S.A.E.

Readers are also invited to submit names of suitable products for health and special diets for inclusion in our information library and for future editions.

VIDEOS by Katherine Monbiot on Vegan cooking are available by post from the publishers at £16 including post and packing.

BOOKS: The number and range of books for further reading are constantly growing. Readers can send a large S.A.E. for the most up-to-date list.

G.S. Publications
Chardstock House, Chard, Somerset TA20 2TL England
Telephone: 0460 63229   Fax: 0460 63809

ABOUT THE AUTHOR

Maurice Newbound sold his publishing business in 1982 and was then able to concentrate on aspects of natural health care in Britain. As President of the Natural Health Network he started the U.K. NATURAL HEALTH WEEK which aims to bring greater awareness of the benefits of a healthy lifestyle. He is catering consultant to the Health Show which takes place annually at Olympia.

In this book he treats you to an insight of his own dietary problems when he discovered, after a serious illness, that he was allergic to meat. Having recovered from nearly three years of disability, he found himself travelling extensively and, at the same time, attempting to avoid all meat products. It was this and the sharing of experiences with so many others with similar problems that encouraged him to write this 'manual' on catering for health and special diets.